90 PERCENT
HALF–TRUE

A COLLECTION
OF SHORT STORIES

D1372591

KEITH PATTERSON

Cosmic Harvest Press
Berryville, VA

Cosmic Harvest Press

Original Cover Painting:
"Salim's Place" by Keith Patterson

For inquiries, please contact
www.cosmicharvest.com

ISBN: 979-8-9857546-1-2

Printed in the United States of America

For my late father, Nathan, who recognized early-on that my future wasn't in baseball OR academics, and kept me well-stocked with pens, paint, and paper since well before my first strikeout.

Wendy,

My friend, thanks
again for spending
some time in paradise.

Much Love,

Keith Pottum.

May 13th 2022

INTRODUCTION

The events unfolded in these tales, the collected shards of my fractured memories, are neither sworn truths nor total fictions. We all know that two different witnesses to the same history standing right beside each other are likely to have differing opinions as to what just transpired before them. Because perceptions, those mirrors to our souls that authors are damned to try and change in others, are born of deeper stuff than mere experiences of perspective. How do you change another person's perceptions? The weight of human experience strongly suggests that this is rarely accomplished by telling the naked truth. So, as an author, I am compelled to call this collection of memories "fiction" even though the survivors and witnesses of these stories, both named and unmentioned, might own differing perceptions concerning the veracity of the situations described herein. And, because these stories were less written by me than gifted to me by The Universe, I can no more vouch for the Absolute Truths included than I can deny actually experiencing these events. The rest is just hyperbole.

CONTENTS

Booboo Gets His   1

Smarter'n Everybody   7

Pine Lake   17

Pecking Order   31

Prospering   43

Backhand Seat   51

Green 3-Piece Corduroy Suit   61

Babysitting for Charley Barrett   71

Electric Fences   81

Cuttin' Wood   89

Who Needs Memories?   95

Thirsty   103

Karma in the Can   117

Crystal's   125

Short Resume   133

Silence   145

Salim's Place   153

The Three Arrows of Time   205

The Clock Tower   219

Booboo, Keith, and baby sister, Amy.

BOOBOO GETS HIS

Pretense: Mental exercise is the unmarried cousin of genteel insanity's descent. It is far better to have a hobby or interest that can sustain you in times of social turpitude. Nevertheless, as a mental aerobics, I tried to pin-point my earliest memory of life service in this earthy realm. I think it might have been when I first realized that I had a little brother...

I guess I knew there was something going on in the crib over by the wall, but I had my own bed and my own issues to deal with and it didn't really confront me until one morning when it did. And there, in the middle of the kitchen, sat my first real memory. It was my fat, brown, red-cheeked baby brother, Booboo. He was sitting in my high-chair. "MY high-chair!"

I could hear my father speaking, and I knew that he was speaking to me, but his words were lost in a fog as I was laser-focused on one goal, "Vanquish the Usurper!"

"Boy, don't you do it! Stay offa that chair!"

Too late. I was climbing-up the side of that high-chair and I was gonna grab that little bum and drag his burbling bu… and that's when the high-chair and Booboo, too, came crashing down on top of me! Booboo's fall was softened by my face and mother scooped him up and consoled him in her loving arms before he could even start crying, which he did anyway, just for effect. Our father lifted the wooden high-chair off of me and lifted me up to console me! "Whoops, misread that."

My father enjoined me with a worn epithet. "Boy, this is gonna hurt me worse than its gonna hurt you." And proceeded to console my bare bottom with his calloused palm. There was a stinging sensation that did not subside even long after the smarting of my rear-end's corporal comeuppance. I didn't have a word then to describe that feeling, but it wouldn't be long before "irony" would be, less a trusted old friend than a constant companion.

"Insult on top of injury" and "salt in an open wound" are also staples of early childhood that only barely begin to describe the ignominy of coming to grips with the fact that "it's not all about me all the time." In fact, it was all about Booboo. I was pretty much on my own, three and a half years old, experienced, hardened, fully aware of the consequences of my actions, a responsible citizen of the world, while Booboo generally got away with being a slobbering, gibberish spewing idiot bent on the destruction of every sacred house-hold norm that had already been painstakingly established.

A few years later, the very first time that I read the

Bhagavad-Gita I realized that Booboo was Shiva, the Destroyer of Worlds. And if my parents had introduced me to Eastern Thought from the get-go then I could have warned them about what that fat, little terrorist was really up to. But the fix was in. Booboo wasn't going anywhere. And, for a while, it WAS all about him.

For two long cycles of the sun there was only injustice and incongruity. Even an omniscient author could see that Booboo was allowed to operate by a different set of rules from the rest of us. He was like royalty. Corrupt, privileged, bloated, birth-right before ability. And as is usually the case when privilege abuses power, it was a short-lived dynasty.

One fine fall day our dear mother announced that we would soon be having a new addition to the family and was somehow blaming it on her fat belly. I couldn't see the connection but, sure enough, next thing you know there she was, a baby sister, about the size of a squirrel with lungs like an ambulance siren. Her arrival instantly rearranged the family dynamic. I already knew where I stood. I was treading water just to stay at the back of the line. But it was Booboo that was having difficulty with the transition this time around.

Booboo descended into a whimpering, slobbering, crying puddle of goo. He had no shame and only wanted his mother. Mom requested that dad take Booboo and I out for a car ride. Dad had to carry Booboo, who was kicking, screaming and crying, over his shoulder.

The car-ride helped to calm Booboo down and by the time that we parked in the lot at Woolworth's Booboo was half-together and balancing a giant snot-bubble on his upper-lip. Dad carried Booboo from the parking-lot and in through Woolworth's big, double entrance doors. He then set Booboo down on his feet in the lobby with a legitimate shot at some dignified autonomy.

The giant snot-bubble on Booboo's lip had been stable but as he stood in the lobby of Woolworth's the bubble on his lip began to grow. "Uh oh." I knew that look. The bubble expanded and contracted with increased frequency as Booboo's face turned red and began to glow! Then Booboo dropped down on the tile floor of Woolworth's lobby and began running around in a circle with his ear on the floor as the axle of a turning wheel, screaming like a banshee and spinning like a top until he finally hit a puddle of his own slobber and skittered-off under a clothing-rack of women's blouses, where he remained, crying, sniveling and barking until my father lifted him up from his textile refuge.

Dad held Booboo in one arm, removed his britches in a blink and did justice upon Shiva, open-handed, with a combination of speed and intensity that had not been seen in this universe since my watch began. And as quickly as sweet justice's recompense, it was over. Booboo's britches were replaced, and he was set down on his feet, once again, in the lobby of Woolworth's.

Booboo was breathing hard, but he was no longer crying. His snot-bubble was gone. Dad held my hand and I held hands with Booboo and the three of us went ahead and did some shopping. After Woolworth's we went and got ice-cream cones. There was more to our shared satisfaction than just the sweet delight of frozen dessert. Dad, Booboo and I were united in the knowledge that there are consequences for our actions and the playing field is level occasionally. And since Karma generally plays out over the course of many lifetimes, it's always especially sweet when it comes back around and bites somebody ELSE in the bum while you can still recall the details of their crimes. And every once in a great while, the long arm and calloused hand of justice serves us up some ice-cream. I got mine. And Booboo got his.

SMARTER'N EVERYBODY

A cool, windy, sun-splashed day in the middle of the first March since my father's passing started me to reminiscing about a formative father/son moment from my childhood. And while there were many moments that I shared with my father that helped to encourage, discourage, guide and mold me, the story about to unfold will reveal the moment when we both knew exactly who I was.

In later years I became very close to my father. As a child I wouldn't say that we were as close. And I certainly don't place the blame for that on him as I was a difficult child to be close to. I spent all of my time either inside of my own head or drawing doodles and pictures on every available surface within my reach. My father was a baseball guy and wanted to bond with me through baseball and I couldn't give a lick about baseball. Plus, I showed absolutely zero talent at any facet of the game and a firm reluctance to pursue improvement. Sometime about the middle of my sixth or seventh year of human service, during the Johnson Administration, my parents began to recognize that baseball was never going to be my thing and signed me up to be a Cub Scout.

The Den Mother of our Cub Scout Troop, Sary Koons, was a hard-drinkin', chain-smoking, pool-shootin', hell raiser of a woman and the mother of my meanest friend, Johnny. Sary was married to Jiffy Koons of Jiffy Koons and the Koonskinners, a second-rate regional touring opening act on the semi-big-time Country Music scene. They were always off touring in their big bus and left the smaller touring van at home with the family. Sary Koonz would cram her clutch of us Cub Scouts all in the van and off we'd go. Our Cub Scout troop spent most den meetings at truck-stops and billiards lounges. And while I did learn a lot in Cub Scouts that fall and winter, including how to smoke filter-less and shoot pool behind my head, I was just holding-out, like every other scout in the troop, for the 1st of spring and the Cub Scout Kite Contest.

There were two categories that you could enter in the Cub Scout Kite Contest: Highest Flying Kite and Best Decorated Kite. I was all over it and laid out my plan for victory and world domination. I think it crossed my mind that after my huge victories in both categories I'd definitely get invited to appear on the Ed Sullivan Show the next time that the Beatles were on. In typical OC narcissistic fashion, my enthusiasm became maniacal and all-consuming. I spent every available moment bent to consummating my vision.

My father recognized an opportunity to bond with me and cheerfully offered me encouragement and advice. "Don't you think you ought to build your kite or at least design it first before you decorate it? And… what IS that, anyway, that you're drawing there?"

Burning rage raced up my spine! The insolence and stupidity on display threatened to make my head explode! I did my breathing exercises and struggled mightily to keep my cool. "'What IS that?' Had the man completely lost his mind?" I had been doodling for days and my masterpiece was nearly complete.

"And Son?..."

"Oh God, here it comes!"

"I don't think you want to build your kite out of that piece of drawing paper that you're working so hard on there. It's too small and it'll just rip apart before it gets off the ground."

"That's it!" For a white-hot moment I thought for sure that my head had exploded and was genuinely surprised that it was still on my shoulders. I wisely held my tongue and kept my thoughts to myself. "Frickin' moron baboon no-nuthin' meat headed ding-dong!"

"C'mon, Son. Let's go up to the hardware store and buy some materials. I've built a few kites in my day and I'll betcha that, together, we're gonna build the best darn kite in Cub Scout History!"

"Ed Sullivan will see right through this yahoo. I'll make sure he stays at home."

At the hardware store we picked-out some Balsawood sticks for a frame and two yards of heavy brown paper off of a big roll. "We already have some glue back at home and we can make the tail out of an old sheet."

Despite my father's misguided attempts to get in the way, kite construction began in earnest.

We checked-out a book from the library about how to build kites. We chose a design and then my father and I built two identical kites. The first one that was finished was our practice kite. The second kite was the one that got the serious decoration and would be the kite that was actually entered in the contest. The weekend before the big event my father and I went over to the high school athletic field with the practice kite.

"Son, let's decide which way the wind is blowing and then turn so that the wind is blowing straight into our faces."

"Oh, great. Now he's probably going to ask me to spit."

Now walk into the wind and let the kite trail behind you while you let-out a little string."

I complied but deep in my core I knew that it was "ALL WRONG!"

"That's right, Son. Now let out a little string and let go of the kite and she ought to lift right on up."

I couldn't breathe. I was living a lie. None of it made

sense. "Walking into the wind? What chicanery!" I fought against fate as long as a mortal can. And then, trusting instinct over superstition, I turned around and ran in the opposite direction. The wind was at my back and so was the practice kite. It smacked me in the head with every stride I ran. Somewhere in the distance I could hear my father yelling for me to turn around and come back. That wasn't going to happen.

The kite stayed pinned to my back, smacking me in the head as I ran with the wind towards the woods at the far end of the athletic field. When I was finally forced to stop running by the presence of a chain-link fence the kite finally cleared my head AND the fence and crashed into a tree. The heavy, brown paper was ripped, and the Balsawood vertical spine was broken. The practice kite was ruined.

After I'd climbed the chain-link fence and retrieved the ruined practice-kite as my father instructed, as he and I walked back across to the far-side of the big athletic field where our car was parked, my father said, "I hope we learned something today."

I could hardly wait to hear what was going to follow. "Probably some Podunk homily about lift and aerodynamics or some rubbish. What a Charlatan."

"Son, we both know that you're pretty smart."

I tried not to roll my eyes at his sanctimony as I was thinking, "Get on with it, man!"

"But Son, folks have been flying kites for a long, long, time. And all of the successful ones have done it exactly the same way, every time. They walked the kite into the wind and let the kite go behind them. That's the way that it's done. Do you really think that you're smarter'n everybody?"

"Was this a trick question?" Now at an early age I knew logic to be a fickle mistress. And the obvious fact that I knew some things that others do not is logically supported by the fact that everybody else knows plenty that I don't know. I had a moment of clarity concerning my father's clumsily leading interrogatory.

The day of the Cub Scout Kite Contest finally arrived. It was cold and bright and windy. Perfect kite-flying conditions. This contest was a really big deal. My entire family was in tow, including my mother, father, little brother and baby sister. We arrived on-time, registered unscathed and along with a throng of jacked-up Cub Scouts and their representatives, presented my kite to the judges.

I recognized several of the scouts from my den and some guys from school that were in other dens. There were kites of every known design and in every conceivable palette and motif. There was a bright red box kite painted with a golden dragon. There was a black and white kite with two vertical spines and three tails that was decorated with the Jolly Roger. I had painted the Presidential Seal on my kite, and, just as I had predicted, rode a wave of patriotism to victory in the Best Decorated Kite category. "Yes! Half-way home to total victory and world domination! Note to self: remember to ask Ringo about that weird high-hat lick on Love Me Do."

Now, don't get me wrong. I was proud to win the Best Decorated Kite division of the contest. But next-up was the Highest-Flying Kite contest and every real Cub Scout with a Bobcat pin and a roll of twine knew that this was the Big Show. A hundred Cub Scouts strong lined-up across the middle of the same athletic field where my father and I had practiced the week before. Conditions were similar to the day of our trial run. "Remember what we learned last week" my father whispered in my ear. "Walk the kite into the wind and let the twine out a little-bit at a time, just like we practiced. You've got this, Son."

"Can he not give it a rest? What does he think I've been doing, non-stop for weeks on end? Following lemmings and sheep? No, I've been gleaning every morsel of knowledge that there is to know, searching for an advantage. I already knew that everybody else would be walking or running with their kites into the wind. But I was the Cub Scout that was seeking-out the path less-travelled."

"ON YOUR MARKS!" barked the Scout Master as he raised his starter's pistol above his head.

I surveyed the pitch, time standing still as my gaze swept from left –to-right and beheld the gaggle of my

Cub Scout rivals jostling for position.

"GET SET!"

I felt as if I was in a dream. "I have been here before. The Tao finally makes some sense."

"Get ready, Son!" I could hear my father yelling from a fogbank somewhere in the distance.

"BANG!" The Scout Master fired his starter's pistol! I fell to my knees in shock as the entire troop ran into the wind and a hundred home-made kites jumped-up into the bright, sunny, blue sky!

"Get-up, Son! RUN!"

As I regained my feet my brain was processing thousands of calculations simultaneously, seeking to turn this momentary set-back into the impetus for total-victory. My Cub Scout competitors were already far away, and their kites were all high in the sky. Instinct and new hope stole the microphone from that fickle mistress, Logic, and I began to run. I ran as I had never run before, my legs churning and lungs heaving, and I could feel my kite somewhere behind me as I ran wild with the wind in search of fame and glory who were whispering "Until somebody works-out Einstein's whiffs, gravity is just a theory."

I ran with newly found speed and authority but eventually, as I approached the far-end of the field where my practice kite had met its demise the week before, Einstein's error, in the guise of my kite, did then again catch-up with me. "WHAP!" The kite smacked me in the back of the head and kept-on smacking me, forcing me up against the chain-link fence at the end of the field at the edge of the woods. I was trapped between the kite and the fence and was getting slapped around pretty good before my father finally pulled the kite off of me.

As I look back on that memorable day from childhood one thing that stands-out to me is the patience of my father, who, when he pulled that kite off of me, didn't say a word. He didn't need to say a word because he gave me a look that was worth a thousand of 'em. Another thing that stands out to me is that, looking back and trying to be honest, If I could do it all over again, I'd probably make the same move. And my father knew this about me. And the look that he gave me said that he knew this about me. It was the moment that we both knew exactly who and what I was, "smarter'n everybody".

A couple of days after the kite contest my father cornered me at the dinner table for some Q & A. "Son, how many categories were there in that kite contest?"

"Had the old-man gone senile? He and I both knew that there had been two categories!"

"Two, right?"

"That's right, Dad. Two categories." I was barely containing my derision at his waste of verbiage AND my time!

"That's what I thought. Well, you came in first in one out of two categories. That's like batting five-hundred and that kind of average might get you into the Hall of Fame some-day. Nice job, Son."

"Average? Ha! There he is, going for the low-hanging fruit again." Empathy was NOT my father's thing. If he'd had half a clue he'd have known that there was only one thing that I wanted to know from him at that point. "Has Ed Sullivan called?" I never did ask. Now I get to always wonder.

PINE LAKE

A Hotly Debated Memoir

Not every monkey has an uncle, and I can't see Darwin OR his detractors either one laboring to contest that fact. But each of us, from the freethinkers down, has a family. And every family has its' fair share of secrets. And while money and stature can buy your family some time in terms of allowing certain secrets to remain hidden, eventually the truth always comes out. And just as the glamour and power of the Kennedys couldn't conceal or be diminished by the factually-based myth of a defective cousin warehoused somewhere deep in the bowels of Hyannis Port, neither can the years of denial and obfuscation by members of my own family manage to obscure my memory of what I know that I saw one summer's day in my youth at Pine Lake.

I don't pander to mythos. Anybody with half of an imagination can testify to that. And even though my personal reality might be skewed by my unique perceptions, the fact is, I deal in hard realities. One hard reality that I've been dealing with is the fact that I've been trying to write this story for over forty years, but I never had an ending until now. Another hard reality is that Pine Lake is really just a pond. And it isn't even a very large pond. Pine Lake is actually a small pond in an abandoned cornfield surrounded by red-clay mud. About a hundred and fifty yards up the hill from this optimistically-named natural body of water is an old in-ground concrete swimming-pool, a remnant of a long-gone motel deemed irrelevant by the by-pass. But by-pass or no, Pine Lake was the uncontested summer-time mecca to several generations of western Pittsylvania County's finest.

One summers' Saturday afternoon when I was six or seven in the year of our Lord nineteen hundred and sixty-six, my family descended upon Pine Lake. My mother, her mother and father, my mother's younger sisters, brothers, wives, husbands, in-laws, outlaws, my siblings, first and second cousins, third cousins, my dad, his dad and I took over the leisure-time destination in its entirety and then some. Half of us attempted to splash all of the water out of the pool while my two uncles on my mother's side backed-up their truck and put their home-made motorboat into the lake down the hill. My father was lighting a charcoal grill, grinning from ear-to-ear. My mother coated my bare shoulders and back with ointment. As my mother double-coated my back with lotion I heard my uncles down at the lake roar in approval as they successfully started-up their motorboat. I broke free from my mother's clutches and bounded down to the belching boat bobbing up and down in the red-brown water.

My teenaged uncles, Dallas and Charles, were looking quite pleased by the fruits of their efforts. They had been on a mission for over two years to construct a motorboat, put it in the water at Pine Lake, and water-ski. The summer before they had rigged-up an over-sized outboard motor to an old wooden canoe. That motor had also started right up. But Dallas and Charles hadn't quite worked-out the details of a functional rudder or a kill-switch. So, when they fired up the motor the canoe shot straight across the lake with them in it, hit the bank at full-speed and cut a foot-deep groove in the red-clay beach that ran fifty yards down-the-hill to where the canoe finally came to its final resting place. As nearly a quarter of the water in Pine Lake drained- away down-hill through the foot-deep ditch cut by the runaway boat, the engine then exploded and what was left of the canoe and gasoline had burned well into the evening. Uncles Dallas and Charles escaped with some burns and abrasions. Lessons learned. This time around their boat had all of the amenities, including steering, a kill-switch AND a rudder.

"Who wants to be first?" Uncle Dallas threw out the tow line into the red-brown water.

I immediately leaped into Pine Lake. I ran out towards the towline that was visible in the water behind the boat. When the water got over my head I attempted to swim. I couldn't swim. I reckon the water was about four feet deep and that was just a couple of inches deeper than I was. I was down in that murky water ham-paddling nowhere for what seemed like a week. Uncle Dallas finally pulled me up sputtering and shooting water out of my nose.

Dallas said, "Here, you wild thing. Put these on." Then he helped me put on a faded orange life-vest and a pair of skis. After some brief instructions the rudder was dropped, anchor hove, steering-wheel buried hard-left and the slack was taken-out of the towline. Uncle Charles goosed the motor while Uncle Dallas simultaneously let go of me and I WAS UP!... Skiing! And then I was down... under-water... above the water... on the water... refusing to let go of the handle of the towline. We circumnavigated Pine Lake exactly three times before I was beached. Still refusing to let go of the towline, I circumnavigated the bank of Pine Lake once more and then skittered off down the hill following a similar trajectory to that of the previous year's ill-fated canoe, where I came to rest at the base of an elm tree and just lay there like I was dead for a while.

"Hey, kid. You're an animal! Nice ride." Dallas helped me to my feet and removed my life vest. "Get in line and you can have another ride later."

There was a line of people, young and old, family, friend and strangers queued-up for a chance to water-ski in Pine Lake behind Dallas and Charles' home-made motorboat. I just stood there for a while and watched the procession and listened. They had gleaned much from that initial ride that I'd taken. The water was about four-feet deep so they put-out four and a half feet of rudder and basically just let the boat spin around like a top in the middle of the lake. The more experienced skiers were getting more like four times around the lake before getting beached. It looked like a long wait to get another chance to ski so I started walking back around Pine Lake towards the up-hill side. I was covered in red-clay mud and needed to rinse-off. I considered a dip in the lake, but the motorboat and skiers made that difficult. Plus, the lake's water, naturally reddish brown, was taking-on a darker, oily hue. I decided to rinse-off in the pool.

I scrambled up the hillside from the lake and jumped into the pool in the shallow end. As soon as I hit the water people started screaming!

"He's filthy!"

"Get him out!

"EEEWWWW!"

A brown cloud spread-out from my body and filled the shallow end. I could smell and taste the lake water and local mud mixed with what was left of my sunscreen and various ointments as they dissolved into the pool-water, which tasted better than it looked. The nasty comments from family and strangers continued.

"Get him out!"

"EEEWWWW"

"Gross!"

"Geez." It wasn't as if the water in the pool was pristine BEFORE I got in. Then my mother jerked me up out of the pool by my arm and stood me up on the pool's deck.

"Go over there to the shower and clean-off before you get back in this pool! You hear me?"

I hated to disappoint my Mama and started trudging around the deep-end of the pool towards the shower, which was a garden-hose tied to the top of a two-by-four which was stuck in the clay. The sun came out from behind a cloud and its' sudden brilliance blinded me. I had to avert my eyes and looked down at the murky red-brown water-cloud that I'd contributed to the shallow-end as it reached the deep-end, lending a clarifying background hue to the reflection in the water. In the reflection I could clearly see him! He was standing on the concrete deck across the deep-end of the pool from me. It was a monkey-boy!

I was gob-smacked! Stunned! Time stood still. The monkey-boy met my gaze as we both stared at his reflection on the water! He looked to be about my height and was covered from head-to-toe in a fine reddish fur and wearing a special monkey-diaper that allowed his little tail to breathe and wiggle around. I was mesmerized by his whose twitchy movements seemed to mimic my thoughts.

"Comment allez-vous?"

The monkey-boy spoke French! Although I didn't recognize the words, I could intuit the context. But before I could answer the monkey-boy's query, my mother had me by the elbow and was dragging me away. "Time to go home!"

I protested but it was no use. I didn't even get a chance to water-ski again. Some of the locals, family and strangers alike, clapped and cheered as my mother removed me from the premises. And that's not the first time that THAT has happened.

Over these long, fruitless years I have investigated every darkest corner, and questioned everyone that I know, repeatedly. Nothing hearing anything solid. Just lies, innuendo and more lies. I've knocked on doors, put ads in the paper, visited internet chat rooms, tweeted, twerked, Tindered, Face-timed, Snap-chatted, Snack-chatted, Facebooked, Fakebooked, I even launched a commercial website where you can buy Monkey Boy merchandise and hopefully aid me in my quest for answers. I even got into politics without knowing it. A local candidate was having a rally and a bunch of folks were wearing Monkey Boy T-shirts and somebody yelled "DO YOU B'LEEV IN THE MONKEY-BOY OF PINE LAKE?" The candidate replied "Nawwwww. There 'aint no monkey-boy of Pine Lake! Never was and never will be!" They booed him off of the stage and he lost the election. And I've gotten a couple of "hot leads" but nothing has ever turned-out to be the Monkey Boy of Pine Lake. I will surely know him when I see him again. I can guarantee you that.

Since that life-altering encounter across the deep-end at Pine Lake, fifty-some-odd years hence, I have received little solace as I've drifted like a refugee from hint to clue. Many of my older relatives that might have had first-hand knowledge as to my life's answers are now departed from this earthly vigil. And now, our old, ancestral family home is boarded-up and everyone has moved away.

Recently, after a long absence from the fold, I attended a family reunion in North Carolina. The after-dinner conversation inevitably came around to the Monkey-boy of Pine Lake. Those relatives that were old enough to be familiar with the story were still denying it. The younger, more educated crowd were ambiguous. And the younger set were all ears. Nothing new here. Denials and digressions. But then Uncle Dallas, who's somehow survived more than just one canoe explosion to become the Paterfamilias, offered-up an absolute gem!

"I do seem to recall," Dallas began, ensconced in a deck sofa surrounded by family and sniftering the remnants of an iced Scotch. "There was a rich family that lived in a big, white house up-the-hill-a-ways from Pine Lake."

"Yeah.'

"Yeah, I remember that house."

"Yeah"

Uncle Dallas continued, "I know for a fact that those people kept pet monkeys. Treated 'em like family. Those monkeys used to tear that nice place apart. And the bigger monkey DID wear a diaper."

Dallas seemed as sincere as I'd ever seen him.

"Is that really true?" asked a first cousin's wife.

"Sure, that's true," Dallas nodded. "And that's what you saw that day, nephew. It was them rich people's big monkey. And I remember that monkey had a little tail, too."

"Yeah, I remember that big monkey."

"Yeah, me too."

"Yeah, that's what you saw. It was them rich people's big monkey."

Something didn't jive here. I'd never heard this story before. "Why now?" My head swam. I'd asked this same crew for answers a hundred times. It was some vast conspiracy, spanning generations. Then a vital clue popped into my head. "But, the monkey-boy of Pine Lake spoke French!" I blurted. "How do you explain THAT?"

Uncle Dallas replied calmly and authoritatively, "Those rich people were French. 'LeFleur' I believe it was. That's why that big monkey of theirs spoke French."

A stone in every pathway. I felt sick and needed to sit down. The festive gathering continued without my further input as I struggled to keep my composure. This was my biological family, and I couldn't trust anyone.

Maybe an hour passed. Uncle Dallas found me and whispered in my ear. "The monkey story was just a smokescreen." Dallas looked me squarely in the eyes. He was serious. "Go back to your old family home. It's all boarded-up."

"I know," I replied.

"Well, there are some other things that you need to know. Those things are hidden away in the secret cellar underneath of that house."

"Secret cellar?"

"Be quiet and listen!" Uncle Dallas clutched my shoulder and looked around suspiciously. He had been a butcher by trade and his hands were still strong from his life's work. "There's a crawl-space opening around back behind the azaleas. Bring a flashlight. You gotta crawl to your left and go three right turns around the original foundation and then you'll see the stairs down. The door is open. You'll find-out everything that you want to know. Now, that's it. It's done. I don't ever want to hear about the Monkey-boy of Pine Lake EVER AGAIN!" Dallas turned away quickly and was gone. And as of this writing I have not seen or heard from him again.

On my way back home from the reunion I rerouted through western Pittsylvania County. First, I drove out to Pine Lake, parked, and walked around. It actually looked much the same as it did fifty years ago, but smaller, abandoned and derelict. I stood on what was left of the crumbling concrete pool-deck, looking across the deep-end to where I'd seen the Monkey-Boy of Pine Lake so many years before. It was about the same time of day as that original encounter. The sun was high in the sky blinding me. I had to divert my eyes downwards to the surface of the dirty-water in the deep-end. I could see my own reflection.

I looked around what was left of Pine Lake a little more, reminiscing and searching for memories, and then got back in my car and drove over to the old-family home, down the Blair Loop Road off of Westover Drive. I parked, grabbed my flashlight, walked around back and found the crawl-space door behind the over-grown azaleas. I lifted the latch, swung open the door, turned-on my flashlight, swatted away years of cobwebs and crawled under the old house. It took a while for my eyes to adjust to the harsh beam of my flashlight juxtaposed with the otherwise total darkness. I crawled on my hands and knees and struggled to follow Uncle Dallas' instructions. The passageway was narrow and rocky. "Three rights." It was stifling. My knees and hands hurt. Cobwebs were everywhere. I was hoping not to meet up with a snake. At last, I rounded a third corner of the original foundation. And there it was! A narrow stone stairway down to the dank opening of the old home's original cellar.

I took a deep breath. The dank air was dead and stale. I made my way down the steep, narrow stairs, pushed aside the old wooden-plank door and stepped inside. A quick flash-light sweep of the carved-out stone walls revealed no major menace or surprises. There were several broken things and an old, rusted boiler. There was a rickety shelf with one Mason jar and an old seaman's trunk covered in decades of dust. I tried to remember if Uncle Dallas had given me any clues that I'd forgotten. I couldn't remember anything. I swept the flashlight over the walls again. Then the ceiling and floor. Nothing new immediately jumped to my attention. I was a little bit relieved. And a little bit disappointed. Again, I shone my light on the Mason jar up on top of the rickety, wooden shelf. It was two-thirds filled with a pale, yellowish liquid. There was something submerged in the liquid, and I strained to see what it was. The shelf on which the jar was resting was too high-up for me to reach. "If it would just float to the top of the jar, I could see what it is." I thought. Then the object in the liquid floated to the top of the jar! Instantaneously I had to tend to an itch at the base of my spine and my flashlight beam fell away as I scratched myself. The beam of light fell upon the ancient seaman's trunk. There was no lock on it, so I opened it up. There was no pirate's treasure inside. Only neatly filed papers. They were medical bills. For expensive ointments and lotions. And electrolysis treatments. There was also a medical journal with a page marker. I opened the book to the marked page and read the high-lighted words. "At any time, any mother can birth offspring with mutations that reveal traits of any ancestor along their evolutionary tree."

"What could it mean?" I put the papers back in the trunk, dragged the trunk over to the high, rickety shelf, climbed-up on top and retrieved the Mason jar. I carefully climbed down from the trunk, set the jar down on a low ledge of the stone wall and retrained my light on whatever it was that was inside. I stared at it for a while but did not fully comprehend. It looked like a skinny, little pickle covered with fine, red hair. I jiggled the Mason jar with one hand while I held the light with my other. When the hairy, little pickle jiggled in the amber brine the itch returned to the base of my spine. Realization began to descend upon me, and my entire world began crashing down. All of the denials, deceits and outright lies cascaded through my mind like an avalanche of pain, doubt and disbelief. All of these many years, my family, the lying, denying lot of them, had only been trying to protect me.

I must have passed out for a while. When I awoke, I

was lying flat on my back on the cool stone floor of the secret cellar. It was dark as pitch. My flash-light batteries were completely dead. I crawled out and up the stairs of the hidden cellar, reversed directions, make three lefts, and finally found the door to the crawlspace. I retrieved a pack of matches and some fresh flash-light batteries from the glovebox of my car and went back to re-enter the secret cellar. I wanted to retrieve the treasures of my life's sojourn. As I re-entered the crawlspace behind the azaleas, I lit a match. It burned-out quickly so I threw it down and lit another. The light from the second match revealed that the first match that I'd tossed had landed on an old rag. The smelly old rag ignited, and I could now see the solvent can near the flames! I scrambled out and away from the old, frame house as it was quickly engulfed by fire. I had to move my car to keep it from also being lost and just kept on driving, I could hear the wailing of the firetrucks and police cars as I took the back-roads home where I immediately sat-down to finish this story.

Epilogue: Thank-you, Uncle Dallas, should you ever read this, for helping me to finally lay to rest the quest that had so consumed me. But while I finally have an ending for my story, I still lack closure. Now I have an entirely new scenario to ponder and for future reference I will set aside my books by Darwin and crack-open the Pavlov. For every time I hear the wail of ambulance, firetruck or police-car sirens, I have to scratch an itch at the base of my spine

PECKING ORDER

Timing is everything, especially when it comes to getting a haircut before the beginning of a new school year. In Northern Virginia it's the same as anywhere else. Get that trim too early and by the first day of class your shag says that you just don't care. Get that cut too late during the summer break and every lump and deformity of your pate is exposed to public scorn and social ridicule. For many years I suffered until the summer before fifth grade when the stars aligned and one evening, three weeks before the start of school, I realized that my hair wasn't in my eyes but was just long enough to hide my most egregious cranial conflagrations. I was already celebrating my impending ascension of the local, grade school social pecking order, but, as is my wont, I had spiked the ball a little too early. And as I combed-out my feathered forelock in the bathroom mirror my father called us in to the dinner table for a family meeting where he announced, "I've taken a new job. Start packing. Day after tomorrow, we're moving to Mississippi!"...

Saying goodbye to our old friends was difficult. They would not be forgotten. Driving over eleven-hundred miles down to the gulf coast of southernmost Mississippi in a '65 Chevy Wagon, devoid of air-conditioning during the super-heated depths of deepest July, with three kids, two parents and a dog was more difficult than the goodbyes. And then, the family's arrival at our new home in Ocean Springs, in a new housing development built on silt that was dredged up from the bottom of the Gulf of Mexico at the mouth of the mighty Mississippi River, was a hot slap in the face.

I thought that it had been sweltering INSIDE of our tin Lizzy but when I opened the door, stepped outside, and stood in the driveway of our new home, the afternoon Mississippi heat hit me hard on the head. I was closer to the sun than I had ever been before, and I sensed the special vengeance that Ra held for this place. "WHAP!" Something smacked me in the head! "YEEOWWWW!" Something bit a chunk out of my crown, and it hurt like heck!! I struggled to get a flying beast about the size of my middle toe out of my hair. I found out quickly that deer flies were the worst in the heat of the late afternoon. And horse flies, as big as my thumb and with a bite than can leave scars and pain that lasts a lifetime, are extremely active in the relative coolness of early morning.

We dodged deerflies and started unloading our station wagon. As my mother and little sister walked the dog and my younger brother, Booboo, and I helped dad get our essential gear inside our new house, a crowd of local kids on bicycles began assembling on the road in front of our driveway. They were eyeing us warily, but nobody made any remarks about the shape of my head. My haircut was holding serve. At some point my dad was inside of the house and my mom, little sister and our dog were around back, and it was just me and Booboo facing the local bike gang rabble. The kid with the long skinny face and big teeth spoke first. "Hey jerk! What's your name? And what should we call your fat little brother?" The other brazen rascals giggled and laughed.

I was momentarily nonplussed, but my younger brother, Booboo, a natural target, was a more practiced veteran of these situations and instantaneously returned his standard response. Booboo turned around with his back to the locals, stuck out his ample rear and gave 'em the ol' "Nanny Nanny booboo, stick your nose in doo--"

"WHUMP!" Booboo didn't even get to finish the clincher before the skinny headed kid with the big teeth tackled Booboo into the sand and silt of our new front yard. Sworn to protect my little brother I took the opportunity to jump on his assailant, at which point a bigger kid from the biker crew jumped on top of me. It was me and Booboo, two on two against our welcoming committee and we began to get the upper hand. Then the biggest kid in the pack, a long-haired rangy animal, took charge of the proceedings and ended-up smacking me around while sitting firmly upon my chest. I was losing considerable spit and felt the last of my baby teeth start to loosen up before my father stepped outside and formally requested an end to the umbrage. All participants wiped some dirt off and it was time for official introductions. "My name is Jimmy Kegny," said the kid with the skinny head. "I'm Billy Banks," said the first kid that had jumped on me. My father extended his hand to the rangy, long-haired kid that had sat on my chest and slobber smacked me around pretty good.

"And what is your name, my dear?"

"Beth Banks, Sir."

"My dear? Beth? What the…" It was then that I noticed that the long-haired rangy kid was a girl.

We only had two weeks of summer left to investigate our new surroundings before the start of school and me and Booboo took advantage of every waking minute exploring on our bikes as far as they'd take us and on foot until we were forced to swim. There was a thousand yards of bayou between our street and the Gulf of Mexico, where the brackish bayou waters mixed with the salty gulf, and we turned over every rock and stump we encountered. We made friends and got into fights with new enemies. Then we'd get into scuffles with our new friends. Booboo nearly got eaten by an alligator that lived in a swampy pond not far from our house. It was a truly glorious time in life. Then school started.

Fifth grade at Ocean Springs Elementary was largely forgettable. I had done this work the year before. Booboo too. We were all about getting home, jumping on our bikes, and seeing where our legs could take us. One day after school we ended up deeper in the woods and waters than we'd ever ventured before. Spanish moss hung thick on the branches of ancient cypress trees whose gnarled roots rested in the shade of the dark bayou waters below us. Thousands of fiddler crabs scurried across the dirt road at our feet, hurrying from tide pool to estuary and back again. Seventy-five yards away, down at the waterline on the shore just around the next bend, were several crude sheet-metal shacks and a couple of pontoon boats moored at a long dock beside them. Two young, bearded men in a john boat with an electric motor pulled up to the dock and tied off. They unloaded a cargo of fish and crab pots and disappeared into one of the shacks. I was transfixed. Time seemed to stand still. The air was filled with the sounds of birds and insects. Then Booboo and I heard someone approaching from behind us!

We both jerked our heads around and beheld two young girls, about our ages, riding up on rusted old bicycles. They stopped right next to us, smiling and giggling and whispering amongst themselves. They had to be sisters. They had beautiful dark bronze skin, long, curly reddish-brown hair and green eyes. Their movements and voices were enchanting. My jaw hung open upon my chest wherein my heart pounded in an unaccustomed manor. The older girl spoke first. Her accent was strange. She asked me my name. After a painful eternity I was finally able to answer her. And then the four of us began talking like old friends and in a precious few minutes learned all that we could about each other. Their family name was Gautier, just like the local township. Their family had always lived in this bayou. And then our revelry was broken by a man's voice from down at the dock yelling, "CINDY! KATRINA! GIT YAW DUN HE NAW!" And then the girls were gone like a shot and me and Booboo decided that it was probably time for us to get moving along ourselves.

We had a difficult time making our way back home. We were lost to begin with and then the tide had come in. We had to drag our bikes through water we had earlier pedaled across. As Booboo and I lay in our bunkbeds that night, we talked about the day's adventure. Fifty years later, Booboo and I are still talking about it. But the beautiful creole sisters living in the tin shacks deep in the bayou necessarily took a backseat to the next day's new find. That new find would be a visit to the rustic home of our new friend, Greg Webb.

Greg Webb lived with his grandmother in the woods about a hundred yards from the back of our house. Greg always went barefoot and actually had webbed feet. He was a real good swimmer. His grandmother claimed to be a witch and had human skulls displayed upon every available interior surface. She said that the skulls were mostly those of Chickasaw Indians whose burial mounds had been destroyed by the construction of the new neighborhood that we lived in. One day when I was visiting Greg, Grandma Webb looked up from jabbering some incantations, looked at me squarely through the glaze of her lidded slits and prophesied, "ALL OF YOUR NEW HOMES WILL SOON BE DESTROYED!" Then she started cackling and rolled herself a cigarette. In retrospect, Grandma Webb's prophesy of imminent destruction should have had more gravitas upon my decision making. But in the moment, it didn't hold much sway with me and I didn't mention it to anyone. I had other plans for that night.

One of my new friends was an older kid named Chip Meiser. Our fathers worked together, and we were encouraged to hang out with each other. And so, we conspired to have an adventure. I told my parents that I was staying at Chip's house, and he told his folks that we were at my house, and we stole off down to the beach at dusk and borrowed somebody's sailboat that was tied up on the shoreline. We headed out into the Gulf towards the barrier islands a few miles off of the coast, raiding crab pots along the way. We had water-proof matches and two empty gallon coffee cans and boiled crabs on the beach of Dauphin Island. We feasted, fell asleep and woke-up predawn to a million flies all over us and our crabby refuse. We jumped back on the boat and started back towards the mainland and that's when our adventure really began.

Chip and I were both experienced sailors and the prevailing wind had made sailing out the nine or ten miles to Dauphin Island rather easy. But getting back was near impossible. We tacked back and forth relentlessly and barely made any progress. Then we'd tack too hard and swamp the boat, which was a small catamaran. Our combined weight was barely enough to raise the mast up out of the water when we both hung off the raised pontoon. We repeated this course of action ad infinitum until we were exhausted. After one dunking I nearly drowned. When we made it back to the shore I fell down, kissed the sand and took a nap, face down. When I awoke Chip was gone. When I finally dragged myself home about noon, nobody asked me where I'd been, and I didn't offer up any explanations. There was no need to manufacture any trouble. Unbeknownst to me, plenty of trouble had already been manufactured.

The crab pots that Chip Meiser and I had pilfered all bore the same mark "HH" in red, painted capital letters. We didn't know it then, but they belonged to a waterman named Hermes Hague, who was also the local magistrate. The word on the street was that old man Hague was out for blood. He took his crab pots seriously and was going door to door looking for answers. One evening Hermes Hague knocked on our door. I could hear him talking with my father on the front porch. "What is it, Hermus?"

"Somebody dun rob my pots 'tween here and Dauphin Island. I know damn well fer sertin' it's 'em damn, thievin' Gautier boys! You hear tell a dem or anyone dat my know sumpm you tell me, and I be much oblige."   The   tough-looking   leather-faced   old waterman looked-up at the night sky and said to my father, "It's de calm 'fore de stawm. Gon' be a big 'un. Might wanna go inland summers iffn' ya got som place. Bon soir." Hermes Hague left our front porch and hurried off to the next house on our street before I showed my face. My father asked me and Booboo straight up if we knew anything about Hermes Hague's crab pots or the Gautier boys. Booboo lied once. I lied twice.

The next morning the wind started blowing. Fishermen returned to their ports and put the word out. It was the biggest storm that anyone had ever seen. Every local agreed with what Hermes Hague had told us the night before. We loaded-up some essentials and headed inland to the brick home of a generous friend. At the inland edge of the narrow swampland causeway that connected Gautier Parrish to the mainland we passed by the sea-level home of Hermes Hague. He had chained himself and a cooler of beer to a pylon that was his stilted home's main support, as was legendarily his custom when Poseidon was angry. He raised his PBR, and we waved as we passed by.

The fierce night that followed will never be forgotten by those who survived it. Many hundreds did not live to tell. The hurricane that laid waste to the Gulf Coast was named Camille. The region hadn't seen anything like it for over two-hundred years. It was three weeks before we could attempt to return to our home. Hermes Hague's house on stilts was gone. All that remained was the massive pylon to which he and his cooler of beer had been chained. Along the causeway only a few telephone poles were left standing. Those that remained were draped with seaweed and debris. There was no hope that our home could be left standing. My mother and father both wept as we drove slowly towards whatever remained.

Miraculously, our house was still standing! Of the eighty some odd new homes in our neighborhood, at least sixty were simply gone. Vanished without a trace. The rest were damaged to some degree but ours was livable. There was no electricity for several months but somehow life struggled on. Greg Webb's house, where he'd lived with his grandmother the witch prophet and a hundred human skulls, was gone from this earth. The bayous were an unrecognizable desolation. Inlets were jetties and vice versa and homeless snakes and alligators were everywhere. Booboo and I were forbidden to venture far from home so as soon as we could sneak away, we set out on our bicycles to find Cindy and Katrina, the Gautier sisters.

We tried to retrace our path to the peaceful stretch of bayou where the lovely Gautier sisters called their home, but the bayou had been completely rearranged by the monster storm. We came to a spot that we thought we recognized. We would have to jump a stretch of water and land on the lower far bank. I retreated on my bike, gathered some momentum, and easily made the jump. Booboo followed suit, made the jump but landed badly and collapsed in a groaning heap. His handlebar had jammed him up under his rib cage and he laid there like he was dying, unable to speak and barely breathing! I had to make a decision. I knew that the tide was coming in so I dragged Booboo up to some higher ground and left him to go and get help.

There was no way to jump my bike back over the rising water to the higher bank on the other side of the jetty, so I swam for it. The current swept me straight out towards the sea. I fought against the tide, but I could sense my own futility and prepared to die. Then, out of nowhere appeared a john boat. Strong hands lifted me from the surging waters. I recognized the bearded faces of my saviors. It was the Gautier brothers.

The Gautier brothers took me straight to the dock at what was left of the magistrate's office. Hermes Hague, who'd survived the storm chained to his foundational pylon, was on the job. I told Mr. Hague what had happened and where Booboo lay dying and that the Gautier brothers had saved my life. Hermes Hague, me and the Gautiers got in their boat, and we went and rescued Booboo. The hospital in Biloxi was notified and they sent an ambulance and Booboo got his ruptured spleen removed before it killed him.

People said that Hermes Hague was a different person after the storm. I was still the same. I never did 'fess up to stealing from his crab pots. This attempt at history must suffice for that. The next time that I saw Beth Banks she was wearing a skirt and looked kind of... I don't know... pretty. I wasn't particularly interested in girls yet. But I did consider beating up her younger brother Billy just so Beth might smack me around a little bit in retaliation. Because, while I'm no psychologist, I do know this much. No matter the what, why nor where, it's a real comfort to know your place in the pecking order.

PROSPERING

Jim Crow sounds like a silly, harmless cartoon character that we watched on TV and laughed at on Saturday mornings. As a child, I heard the term used, but I never put it together relating to people and events in the narrow focus of my own life, which consisted mostly of running backroads and bayous, hunting and fishing, and cooking up adventures to ward off the boredom of small-town rural life. My concerns and wants were my own. "If you want something bad enough," my father would say, "then make a plan and go get it. Nobody's standing in your way." And, while it was true that Jim Crow wasn't blocking MY path, I can now look back and see the claw marks left on the necks of others and the destruction of their dreams and plans. Plans are cheap. Everybody has one until you get punched in the face.

"ALRIGHT! BREAK IT UP!" barked Coach Jenkins. I was swinging my fists in a wild rage, making no contact like I was fighting a ghost, tears blinding my eyes and my mouth stinging as I tasted my own blood.

"I said BREAK IT UP!"

I paid the coach no mind and kept on throwing hands.

No success. BAM! I got punched in the mouth again, just as I finally landed a punch of my own. Pain shot through my fist and up my arm. The ghost was wearing a football helmet.

A big, strong hand grabbed me by the neck of my shoulder pads and lifted me up off the ground. I kicked and thrashed around for a few more seconds and then gave it up. Coach Jenkins set my feet back down on the hard-packed dirt of our practice field. I wiped the tears and snot off of my face. I could see my antagonist slapping high-fives with some other teammates.

"JEROME! Get your narrow ass over here, NOW!" Jerome Jenkins was the coach's son. He walked slowly back over to where the coach and I were standing. "Now shake hands, Godammit, and forget this mess. We're all on the same team, for Christ's sake. Ya'll better save some juice for the game, tomorrow. The Tigers are in first place and looking to kick y'all's asses!"

Jerome and I shook hands. He was probably our best player. I was down that list a few notches. Jerome was our starting halfback, and I was the starting safety. In the second half of games that we were winning, I played halfback and Jerome played safety. We were always getting tangled up at practice and this wasn't our first fight. If I had won this fight, then THAT would have been a first.

"Alright, Jerome. Give your helmet to Keith. Keith,

Give your shoulder pads to Jerome. Let's line up and work on that same play, twenty-three crossbuck. And NO BULLSHIT!"

Jerome and I traded gear and thought nothing of it. Then we rejoined the rest of the team at the line of scrimmage and finished practice without further incident.

We were playing in the twelve and under youth football league in Southern Mississippi in the 1960s. Looking back, everybody was poor back then. After hurricane Camille flattened the region, everybody was even poorer. We had to share equipment. One kid got a helmet, another kid wore the shoulder pads. A couple of lucky dogs got to wear pants with hip pads. A few more had pants with knee pads. We had no real uniforms. We wore our fathers' old T-shirts with our numbers painted on in blue house paint. We were the Generals. The Tigers had real uniforms. Red jerseys with black numbers. Most of their players had helmets AND shoulder pads. We didn't worry about that injustice. We just knew that it was going to be a tough game.

Mississippi was segregated back then. I had no idea of what that meant. At the school I attended, there were only white kids. I didn't question that. Our football team was a mixture of white, black and brown. I didn't question that, either. Coach Jenkins was black. He was a good coach and didn't play favorites. If you could play, then you would get your opportunity. And if you had to play the first half without a helmet, then, by God, you got to wear one in the second half, no matter what color you were.

On Saturday morning I carefully strapped on my shoulder pads and pulled on my makeshift jersey. I looked at myself in the bathroom mirror and practiced a menacing scowl. My busted lip gave me a savage look. I was ready for the Tigers. Mom drove me to the game.

Before the game, Coach Jenkins called the team over to his pickup truck. On the door of the truck was a painted sign. It read "Jenkins' Automotive". Coach Jenkins owned a well-known garage and towing business. Most everybody I knew took their cars to Jenkins' Automotive for repairs and service.

"Boys, today is a big day. And I got a surprise for you." Coach took a cardboard box out of his truck, laid it on the ground and opened the lid. "Look for your number. Everybody gets one!"

REAL JERSEYS! A roar went up as me and my teammates tore through that box! I found my number, 25, quickly pulled off my hand-painted T-shirt and pulled my new jersey over the top of my pads. The jerseys were clean and beautiful, bright blue with big white numbers, front and back. On the left sleeve of each uniform was printed "Jenkins' Automotive". And on the right sleeve it said "Generals". I don't think I've ever been so proud.

The Tigers didn't have any black or brown players. I could hear them calling us names that I would never repeat. No matter. They didn't stand a chance that day. We were jacked to the moon and played like champions! I scored a touchdown in the second half and Jerome hugged me like a lost brother. That night I couldn't sleep until I retrieved my soiled blue jersey from the laundry. The next morning, my mom found me sleeping in it. I didn't think anyone or anything would ever wipe the smile off of my face.

Our team really came together after receiving our beautiful blue game jerseys. There was no more fighting at practice. Jerome and I became friends, and we spent some time together, after school, running in the woods and jabbering about all manner of boy stuff. The Generals won our next three games and made it to the championship game where we would play the Tigers and give them a shot at revenge. It was an exciting time. I lived to go to football practice, and especially to put on that blue jersey on Saturday mornings. But there was trouble brewing that I didn't understand.

I started hearing the grumblings. The parents of some of the other kids were resentful that Coach Jenkins was advertising his Auto business on the sleeves of our beautiful, blue jerseys. Then, at the last Thursday night practice before the championship game, Coach Jenkins wasn't there. His wife arrived late in Coach's pickup truck. Jerome climbed slowly out of the passenger's seat. There were tears in his eyes.

"Where's Coach?"

"Yeah, where's coach?"

"He's in jail," said Mrs. Jenkins.

Jerome stared at the ground, tears pouring down his cheeks.

"The police say you boys got to return those jerseys. Bring 'em to the game on Saturday. When all those jerseys are back in this box, the police say they'll let Coach Jenkins come home."

Mrs. Jenkins burst into tears. She and Jerome got back in their truck and slowly drove away. There was no practice.

Saturday morning was bright and sunny, but my heart was in a hole. I pulled on my old dirty T-shirt with the painted-on numbers, and we drove to the game. My father was driving, and he was not happy. My mother was in the passenger's seat with my blue jersey in her lap. When we arrived at the field for the big game, the Tigers were whooping and hollering, their bright red jerseys shining in the sun. The Generals, dressed in our shabby T-shirts, were hanging our heads. We all put our prized blue jerseys back in that cardboard box and played that game. We had nothing. No coach. No fire. No plan. And no uniforms. And we lost that championship game. We lost by a lot.

One of the parents of a Tigers' player was the local police chief. My father had me by the arm as he waded through the celebratory gaggle of winning players, coaches and parents. He walked up to the police chief and asked, "Why is Coach Jenkins in jail?"

The police chief smiled insincerely, spit some tobacco juice at my father's feet and replied, "We got laws in this state. Folks got to obey these laws, or they got to pay the price."

"What law did Coach Jenkins break?"

"We can't have no uppity negroes actin' like they betta'n everybody else. Our culture gonna go right to hell. We got laws to protect decent citizens against the likes of that."

"What law did he break?" my father repeated. He was squeezing my arm, his teeth clenched, barely hiding his rage.

The police chief sneered through his crooked, yellow teeth, tobacco spittle dripping off his lower lip, and replied. "Prospering."

KEITH PATTERSON

BACKHAND SEAT

One Summer, my family drove a thousand miles north, from southern Mississippi halfway to forever up to Danville, Virginia to attend a big reunion that included both my mother's and father's sides of the family and was being hosted at the long-held family home of my mother's side. We arrived the day of the event. Cars and kids and picnic tables were everywhere. On the long ride up the McElheney's familiar gravel driveway I saw at least a dozen that looked like Uncle Earl, my name dad's brother. I'd had a rough couple of years since I'd seen any of these people. I'd spent most of the last two years being grounded for various, sundry and repeated infractions of family protocols and decency. And, as my mother, father, brother, sister and I found our parking spot and opened the doors of our green Chevy wagon and joined in the festivities, I wasn't as exuberant to show my baboon's rear to everybody conceivable as in years past. A monkey on a tether.

Within ten minutes of arrival, I found my cousin, Paul. His family had just come from a funeral for a friend of theirs. Paul and I slipped off from the gathering party and walked down into the woodsy ravine behind the house. Paul produced some local smoke. I think it was dried corn silks. I pulled a corncob pipe out of my pocket. Paul struck a few damp matches until one caught fire and lit the pipe I was pulling on.

"My aunt says that this life here that we're living is really Hell and things will be MUCH better once we're all dead and gone to Heaven," said Paul.

I was thoughtful on that for a quick minute. "Trust me," I replied as I passed the pipe to my cousin. "Even though these corn silks DO seem to be mostly stems and seeds," I said, "this isn't Hell. And if living here on this beautiful earth with pretty girls, and hamburgers, and fried chicken and pickup trucks and having a smoke with your cousin is 'Hell', then what do you hope that Heaven's gonna be like?"

Paul took a toke off of the cob and answered through clenched cheeks as he choked back the sweetly acrid smoke for maximum effect. "I believe… fft… fft," he began, as some smoke escaped from his ears. "I believe… fft… fft. I believe that Heaven… fft." He let out the remnant of his toke and stared off into space, looking as sincere as a thirteen-year-old boy is capable of. "I believe that Heaven is like sitting around a warm fire on a cold, stormy night, with all of your family and friends and the people that you love."

I'd never seen my cousin Paul be so thoughtful and sincere, so I had to break it down for him.

"So, let me get this straight," I said to Paul. "You're

willing to be stuck in the same room with your mom and dad and brothers and sisters and your Aunt Clara for all eternity? Sitting? Eternity is a long time, my friend. I give you about an hour and a half, maybe less."

Cousin Paul looked at me through glazed eyes and said, "It says in the Bible that Jesus promises to prepare a place for us at the right hand of His Father."

"Sounds pretty crowded," I said.

"REEEooooRIP!" It was my father's unmistakable wolf whistle. It carried for miles and meant one thing "all hands-on deck!"

"Time to eat," said Paul. We both popped a Tic Tac and started walking back up the ravine towards the party, emerging from the woods at different spots and intervals to cover our tracks.

Concerning what Paul said about Jesus' Dad having some room at His table, I looked it up. It's somewhere in the second half of The Book, near a couple of mentions about forgiveness of my sins that I'm counting on. Jesus say's that His Father's got room for all of us over on one side of the table, where we're all going to sit quietly on our hands for an eternity once this clown show is over. And I should be a master of that situation by the time I get there, because at MY father's house, and everywhere else he has some sway, next to his right elbow is where I usually took my meals.

Sitting at the right hand of my father was a solitary calling, with no honor in the distinction, lest you count the mad rush of adrenal shame coursing the veins of the caged beast. As I answered my father's whistle, our eyes met, and he nodded towards where I would sit beside him. And sat there I did, forced to endure miles of platitudes from fawning aunts and uncles and cousins unnamed and plentiful, just to get to the meat of it. The feast! The fried flesh, golden and brown, steaming mashed potatoes, gravy, collards, cooked for hours in fatback flavored waters. And I am stuck, once again, sitting at my father's right elbow, wasting a tasty buzz while waiting endlessly for the blessing so the feast can begin.

The McElheney/Patterson family reunion didn't happen very often. In fact, to my memory, it was a one-off affair, never to be repeated, and mentioned in casual conversation even less than that. This was, in large part, because we had to listen to at least four hundred and thirty-seven adults of every size and social misanthropy blab forth endlessly about how much they were thankful for while all the children and old people were salivating like research animals, waiting for the blessing of the patriarchs, of which there were at least two. As I looked around the large front yard of my McElheney grandparents' ancestral home, I could see dozens of picnic tables spread out under the shade of several massive and ancient oak trees, and the wild eyes of the other starving children, their orbs flickering with anticipation tinged with menace, like the shining eyes of hungry alligators in a Mississippi bayou at dusk.

The grating sentiments continued mercilessly beneath the cloudless summer sky. I salivated until I was out. Then I got desperate, then despondent. A basket of hot biscuits was delivered to each table. The aroma was overwhelming. Warm butter salt glistening brown biscuits, on top of the sumptuous smells rolling off of the fried chicken, cornbread, gravy, mashed potatoes and collards. Nobody dared to touch the food before the blessing. To grab a biscuit before the benediction was punishable by death. The torturous, tiresome orations of the elders dragged on and on. Random thoughts floated through my mind. I thought about baseball, and astronauts. And Marilyn Monroe. "She'd make a great astronaut." It occurred to me that I'd once read an article in the paper, or maybe heard someone say that they had read an article, that said the Queen of England was nicknamed "the Mongoose" for her lightning-quick ability to snatch a crumpet. The article also stated that a crumpet was an English biscuit. "Be the Mongoose!"

My father's right knee bumped purposefully against my left leg. "Boy, don't you even THINK about it."

I looked up and met my father's gaze. He knew exactly what I was thinking. He had obviously read the same article about the Queen. I was doomed and I knew it.

"I will starve to death." Once the finality of this future had truly sunk in and I had become one with the knowledge of my own demise by deprivation, it was as if my earthly tethers were loosed. Even though my rear end was firmly rooted to the peeling paint of a pine bench, my spirit was free to roam. And as Uncle somebody or other droned on about being thankful for the food that I was starving from a lack thereof, I slipped off, mercifully, into a daydream...

...I am in the midst of cracked and broken marble pillars, the crumbling remnant of a once epic library, in the company of a great host of scholarly workers, all doggedly struggling mightily to piece and patch together the ripped and broken spine and the missing and torn pages of an ancient leather-bound book. The smoke-filled skyline is visible through the remaining standing marble columns of the ancient public edifice. The aftershocks of the earthquake that has levelled the city roll intermittently through the dust and the din. I am working feverishly to mend these precious pages. The torn tome is written in a script that is strange to me, but I inherently know the value of the work that I am doing. My work is supported by the straining backs of the scholars below me, just as my own back supports the work of those above me. I groan to the burden upon my shoulders as I bend to the work before me. There are no complaints from anyone working in the steaming, rumbling ruins. There is no questioning the stark necessity to complete the task at hand, the restitution and preservation of every recipe ever committed to parchment! My eyes burn from sweat and smoke and I blink...

... I am alone, sitting naked on a porcelain toilet out in a big field. Blazing bright blue skies surround and engulf me. This situation doesn't seem odd, at first. Then, I hear some voices in the near distance. I strain my neck to look around and see who and where the voices are coming from. There is a pavilion, just up the gentle, grassy hill behind me. It is filled with people sitting at a great table, conversing and laughing. I struggle to hear what is being said at the pavilion without raising myself up off of the toilet and exposing myself. There is no toilet paper. I have no clothes. I can't really understand what is being said by the people sitting at the big table under the pavilion up the hill behind me, but I recognize some voices, and some head shapes. The table is filled by everyone that I love and respect, from Gandhi to Grandma Dot. They all sound so naturally at ease, while I am stuck, naked, sitting alone on the porcelain toilet with no paper, and no pants. Anxiety creeps up upon me. I have an anxious couple of moments and then a profound realization hits me. Nobody under the pavilion even knows that I exist. I wave my hands and shout. Then I rise up off of the toilet, naked, and dance around, waving my arms and yelling! Nobody even notices me. Then they notice me...

... "Keith, Son, wake up." My father nudges me with his right elbow. I shake off my dream, Dad raised his voice and addressed the gathering. "I'm going to ask my son, Nathan Keith the Third, the oldest grandchild on both sides of this family, to say the blessing today." My father turned towards me. There was trust in his face and hope in his eyes. I felt kind of sorry for him. In his own way he was so naïve. I just sat there like a lump, blinking and rubbing my eyes until my father gently kicked my foot, leaned in and whispered, "Just like I taught you. No bullshit."

Simple enough. I knew the routine. Same blessing that I've heard out of my father's mouth nearly every day of my life. It isn't just memorized. It's beaten into my skull. "Dear Lord, Bless the hands that prepared and provided this meal. Make us strong with this bounty so we can go out and do your will, which is to love each other. In all of Your many names, Amen." Boom! Just do it! And the angels sing! And we all get to finally eat! But... no. As I bowed my head to lead this congregation in prayer, I heard some different words began to utter themselves from somewhere south of where the limbo bar of my maturity level was set. "GOOD FOOD! GOOD MEAT! GOOD GOD, LET'S EA--"

"BAM!" My father swatted me completely out of my seat with a brilliant backhand sweep of his right hand! He knew the punchline. I'd learned it from him. It was the blessing he did when mom wasn't home.

As I was sprawled on my back in the grass, still too stunned to embrace the remorse and regret that would eventually catch up to me for squandering my father's trust, I could hear voices like angels up above me, swirling through the fog.

"What'd he do?"

"He made a mistake."

"Goofing around with the Blessing?"

"That was his second mistake."

"What was his first?"

"Sittin' in the 'backhand seat'."

KEITH PATTERSON

GREEN 3-PIECE CORDUROY SUIT

Meaning well must count for something. My cosmology, at any given moment, depends entirely upon this most basic of logistical variables, although, I have not one shred of evidence to support the assertion. And the fact that this tale illustrates the inverse of its own thesis statement should come as no surprise. Because I'm a Mama's boy. And she meant well. And I have the dings to prove it.

Mid-way through my sixth-grade schoolyear my family moved from the bayous and backwoods of Ocean Springs, Mississippi up to Alexandria, Virginia, a thousand miles north and just across the Potomac River from Washington, DC. It was late fall, and it was a lot colder in Alexandria than it was back down south on the Gulf Coast. And the styles of clothes that people were wearing were a bit different as well. Now, I'm just spit-ballin' in retrospect here, but, looking back, I guess my mother was trying to kill two-birds with one stone when she took her hard-earned butter n' egg money and bought me and my younger brother 3-piece corduroy suits. Mine was bright green. Booboo's was brown. These were to be our new school clothes for our first day in our new school. And, apparently, my brother and I were supposed to wear those 3-piece corduroy suits every day after that, as well.

The two birds that I believe my mother was trying to snuff with this new wardrobe were dealing with the coldness of the new climate and keeping up with modern fashions. My 3-piece corduroy suit was warm all-right. There was no hint of trouble in the warmth department. But, in the eyes of my new schoolmates, judging by their general reactions to my warm and natty ensemble on that first day at my new school, we may have missed the mark by a minute in the fashion department.

"Who's the pickle?"

"Hey, Jerk Off! You look like a 3-piece booger!"

There was a lot of laughter. Several kids stuck their fingers in their noses and pretended to throw boogers at me. Some of the pretend boogers were real. I felt one lodge in my carefully combed reddish hued hair. My mother said that my red hair was the reason that she chose the green corduroy for my suit. The irony burned. I retaliated like any good southerner and started tossing some boogers of my own. That's when my new teacher, Mrs. Hinkle, looked up from her desk for the first time.

Eight o'clock day one. Busted for throwing boogers before attendance had even been taken. At that moment it looked to me like it might turn-out to be a long day. I was right and THEN some. "BAP!" a spitball hit me in the neck! I turned reflexively to find the source as a booger hit me in the head from my blind side. I jerked my head back around as six or seven spit-wads splashed against the back of my head. Then, the spit-wads and boogers rained down in torrents, many of each varietal sticking to my corduroy suit as Mrs. Hinkle stared down at her attendance logbook through her thick reading glasses. Finally, I snatched a straw from off of the floor and began returning fire with used spitballs. I put one all the way down one kid's earhole and that kid went down like he'd been slain. Mrs. Hinkle looked-up as I pulled a juicy number off of my lapel, sloppy loaded my used straw and stuck one on his forehead as he lay on the floor clutching his ear.

"THAT'S IT!" Mrs. Hinkle roared as she stood up from her desk. She looked furious. She pointed at me and demanded "You go to the principal's office RIGHT NOW!"

It turns out that my visit to the principal's office would be the high point of my day, a respite from the boogers and spit-wads and derogatory remarks about my chartreuse ensemble. But it was a short stay, and I was told to return to Mrs. Hinkle's class. I walked back into class as Mrs. Hinkle was taking attendance. "Nathan Patterson."

"Nathan? What kind of hillbilly name is that?" My classmates all got a good laugh. This was back before

Nathan was a popular name.

"I go by my middle name, Keith," I explained.

"Keith? That's even stupider than Nathan."

"Booger Boy is better than Nathan."

"OR Keith."

"Nathan Keith Pickle Booger."

The spit-wads started back up. I had my own straws and napkins after returning from the office. Every time that Mrs. Hinkle looked down or away everybody in class was letting fly. Most everybody else was aiming at me. I was chewing paper, stuffing straws and spitting wads at a furious rate trying to match the incoming fusillade. I received no quarter and took no prisoners. It was thirsty work and there was no end in sight, so I decided to go nuclear. I salvaged a big slug of spit, lubed up a fat wad of paper tissue and placed it smack dab in the middle of Mrs. Hinkle's forehead.

"NAAATHAAN PATTERSON!" Mrs. Hinkle was staring me down and pointing towards the door. "TO THE OFFICE!"

My second trip to Principal Neblick's office was slightly less pleasant than the first one, but one look at the hundreds of spit-wads stuck between the twills of my green corduroy told Neblick all that he needed to know. "It can be tough being the new kid." said Neblick.

"When's lunch?" I asked.

"You've got a ways to go to get to lunch, Nathan."

"I go by Keith," I corrected.

"Mr. Patterson…" Neblick was looking over the top of his glasses at me. "I don't care what you "go by". I just know that you better "go by" the straight and narrow. That's what "I" know. Now get out of here and don't let me see you in here again."

In the sixth grade at Colonial Elementary, recess is early, and lunch is late. It was my first day of class in my new school and it was already time to go outside for recess. "Things were looking up."

The playground was large and had a full-length hoops court with what had once been two ten-foot baskets. One rim was leaning, and the other was leaning worse. There were no nets. Several kids, all boys, were shooting and rebounding and fiercely chucking-up wildly acrobatic shots at the hoop leaning the least. There was only one ball. It looked flat. I looked elsewhere. There was a large black-top surface with chalk lines where a bunch of kids were playing some dodge-ball type of game. I walked over and watched how the game played for a minute or two and ciphered a key strategy. The game seemed a cross between dodgeball and red rover but also had some dangerous undercurrents that I was vaguely aware of. There was a certain gang element, as well as girlfriend-boyfriend stuff. The basics were pretty straightforward. If you got hit and didn't catch it, you had to change teams and had the opportunity to run down anybody on either team that wasn't paying attention. Or you could run them down even if they WERE paying attention. I thought that I might really be able to do some damage and increase my popularity. Or, at least, really do some damage.

I walked out onto the game court. Some kid instantly threw one at my head with every shred of gristle he had. I easily caught it and surveyed the landscape for weakness. I found my target and let fly. "BONK!" I laid-out a future cheerleader. Some kid in a leather jacket who might have been my victim's boyfriend picked-up the ball and let it fly at my face. I headed it away with my forehead like a soccer player. Now I was free to wreak havoc. I lined up my series of moves to take out as many as possible as I changed teams. It went off almost as planned! Only with more crying. The mob, boys and girls, knocked me down and kicked the crap out of me. By the time some adults rescued me my green corduroy jacket was ripped at the lapel and right elbow. The left knee of my corduroy pants was shredded, as was my knee, which was bleeding down my leg into my sock.

"What's the matter with you?"

"You stupid freak!"

"You're gonna kill somebody!"

Somebody's gonna kill you, Booger Boy!"

"Pickle Boy!"

"Pickle Booger!"

"Freakin' IDIOT!"

I was dimly acquainted that I'd probably missed on a couple of social cues with the dodgeball group, so I decided to go on over and try my luck on the basketball court where things are more basic.

There were a dozen or so boys, all in the fifth and sixth grade, all related somehow and contesting every shot. The ball was too flat to dribble so the game consisted of rebound it and throw-up a wild attempt. The biggest boys were dominating the rebounding close to the hoop and then the flat ball took a crazy bounce and came my way! I tucked the ball up under my arm and started walking to the other end of the court.

"What the?…"

"Where the?…"

"Who the?…"

"You hood-rats go get your OWN ball." I knew there was no other ball. I was making a statement.

"HOOD rat?"

"HOOD rat?"

"Who you callin' HOOD rat?"

"SMACK!" Somebody slapped me in the back of my head. I turned to face the threat and I was surrounded. No way out. I was in the bull ring.

The two youngest of the ballers, twins named Terrell and Darrell Wheeler, worked me over first, darting in and around and behind me, throwing punches and fancy kicks and landing a few. Then, one kid slipped behind me and got down on his knees as his twin rushed me. I fell to the ground where the two fifth-graders kicked me around a bit before I regained my feet. Terrell and Darrell receded and out stepped Anthony Wright. Anthony was a fifth-grader but he was husky and a lefty and styled himself after Joe Frazier. Somebody behind me pushed me and I walked into a big left hook. I counter-punched with a hook of my own and we were both sucking for air. Anthony stepped out and Bruce Wheeler-Wright stepped in. He was more of an "Ali" man and did a fair amount of shuffling before we exchanged blows. Then it was Melvin and Charlie and then came the heart of the order, Lucky Ducky, Fox, Willie Mac, and Big Timmy, I was worn-out. I had nothing left and kept getting knocked down.

"Stay down, Pickle Boy."

"Stay down, Greenie."

I kept getting back up.

Big Timmy stepped into the ring. He had a fist like a ham. I wiped my nose, looked at my own blood and went berserk. I charged straight at Big Timmy. He brought his ham fist down upon my head. Lights out. I came-to sitting at my desk in Mrs. Hinkle's class. Big Timmy had carried me in over his shoulder after dispatching me out on the hoops court.

Class dragged on. The spit-wads continued at a steady pace. I hardly noticed and kept my head down, saving-up spit and spit-wads and waiting for the right moment. Lunch went by like a flash and then we went to the library, where there was so much mayhem that I was more of an afterthought. My chance had arrived. I caught Big Timmy leaning back and yawning and put a spit-wad down his throat. I heard it splat against his uvula. He was at the water fountain for fifteen minutes. After the library we returned to class for Math. And then finally, at long last, the end of the first day at my new school was in sight. Nothing left but a bathroom break and then catch the bus.

I had to pee something awful and hurried straight to the boys' bathroom where I was greeted by many of the individuals who I'd clashed with earlier in the day. I had to pee and unzipped my fly on the way to the urinal. Several boys blocked my path. My weenie was already out of my fly, and I accidentally dribbled a little pee on the floor, splattering some shoes. Before I could blink, a dozen dicks were pissing on me in retaliation. I let loose and a full-fledged piss fight ensued! I represented well but there were no victors in this battle. When the rabble returned to class, Mrs. Hinkle got all incensed and crazy eyed. She climbed up and stood on her chair and hissed like a cat at a dog park. The bell rang.

The bus driver refused to let me ride home on the bus because I smelled so bad. I had to walk home and got there late. My mother met me at the door and beheld what was left of me and my first-day-of–school outfit. "What hap?..." She got a whiff of me and stopped short. There was no need for words. "Go around to the back-door, take off your suit and leave it outside. Then take a long, hot shower. And you don't have to mention this to your father unless you want to. You poor thing." It was the first time in my life that my mother didn't kiss me upon arriving home from school.

It probably saved a great deal of my hide when my dear mother made a solid syllogism concerning fashion and her first son's survival. That was the last time I ever saw that Green 3-piece corduroy suit. And it was never mentioned again.

BABYSITTING FOR CHARLEY BARRETT

"'Vengeance is mine!' sayeth the Lord!" I picked-up on the potential of that little nugget early-on at Vacation Bible School and always kept it close to my heart. And since the humiliations, injustices and disappointments of childhood were heaped as coals upon my head, I have searched ceaselessly for scant good reason to commit this tale to carbon. One such good reason is called the Statute of Limitations.

When I was twelve years old, the opportunity to help the Lord with some of his earthly workload alighted upon my presence in the form of an angel… the Angel of Armaments. On a return-trip home from a family holiday we stopped at a convenience store/fireworks stand, While my parents were inside buying snacks and paying the tab my younger brother and I stuffed some choice ordinance from the unattended outdoors stand into our father's golf bag in the back of the station-wagon and "voila!" my favorite Bible verse got some wings and a chance to see the light of day, although, truth be told, most of our missions involving righteous Godly vengeance and fireworks occurred at night.

Our righteous daylight missions of vengeful indignation included ruining a couple of birthday parties that we hadn't been invited to and at least one party that we HAD been invited to but didn't attend just so we could ruin it. Exploding bottle rockets were our pleasure,

My younger brother, who wishes to remain anonymous, will be referred to as "Booboo" in this history. Booboo and I had received matching, miniature, iron and wood cannon/radios for Christmas the year before. They were ideal launchers for our bottle rockets, and we quickly learned the fineries of successful mobile rocketry, adjusting the angle of launch and damping the recoil as necessary. And as we became masters of artillery, Booboo and I were both still attending Vacation Bible School where I learned about not judging others so that I won't get judged myself. "Vengeance AND a lack of judgement?" I was all-in. And, just as it was becoming obvious to me that I was made for Vacation Bible School, it was also plainly obvious that God had gifted Booboo and I with the blessed bounty of ballistics. Or, at the very least, God had given us the ability to gift ourselves. And then the last day of Vacation Bible School revealed one last gem. 'From those who have been given the most, the most will be expected." That was us. Booboo and I were practiced, provisioned, ready and waiting for "a sign".

Summer turned to fall, and we got immersed in the

fresh brutality of another new school year. Our only salvation was walking to and from school through Finch's Run, the last 400 acres of near wildness for many miles around the sprawling suburbs. Finch's run is where we met, conspired, bought and sold, smoked, drank, hoped to get a kiss and best of all… on the tallest of the dual hillocks in the center was Finch's Hill, the most awesome sledding hill in seven counties. On the lesser hillock stood an impressive antebellum frame house in the middle of five acres of green grass, the Finches' ancestral home. And then a bombshell rumor dropped down from the unforgiving sky and was quickly confirmed as fact. The Finches were selling Finches' Run, ALL of it! The traitorous Finch family had sold out to a company that planned to build condominiums and a golf-course! Our lives were over! Any chance of a decent adolescence was now done and gone! The word on the street was that the Finches were fleeing to Montana and buying a big ranch. My first lieutenant, Booboo, and I plotted a righteous send-off,

Knowing in advance that our parents were going out on a Friday night, we solidified our plans and checked our stocks. Friday night finally arrived. Our parents were going to a show with the next-door neighbors, the Barretts. The Barretts' had lined-up a babysitter for their 9-year-old son, Charley, but the sitter had thought better of it and cancelled at the last minute and the deck got shuffled. Our younger sister was sent to her girlfriend's house for a sleepover, freeing-up Booboo and I to babysit for Charley. "No problemo."

Charley had already had some early training in rocketry and retribution.

The Barretts told Booboo and I to make ourselves at home and that we could eat whatever we wanted to AND, if everything went as planned, Booboo and I would even get paid! As our parents drove off into the night, Charley, Booboo and I only had one obstacle, as far as I could tell, to keep everything from going as planned. It was beginning to rain.

I asked Charley what he wanted for dinner.

"Burnt toast," Charley replied.

"Of course." I knew that. It was all that I had ever seen him eat. I burnt some toast for Charley.

"It's not burnt enough," said Charley.

I put the toast back in the toaster and carefully placed a cookbook on top of it to hold it down. Meanwhile, in the living room, Charley and Booboo were engaged in a gunfight with metal cowboy cap-guns. Charley, out of fake bullets, was forced to throw his gun and knocked over a lamp, breaking off one piece of the ceramic base, shattering the lightbulb and sending shards of glass across the carpet. About this time, I smelled something burning that wasn't toast. The book on the toaster was on fire! I put on a pair of oven mitts, pulled the book off of the toaster and dragged it across the linoleum counter-top and into the sink. I turned on the faucet and put-out the book. The charred remains of Charley's burnt toast popped-up from the toaster in a belch of black smoke,

"Perfect!" said Charley, who poured himself a glass of milk and consumed every last bit of crisped carbon crust.

Booboo and I had already eaten dinner, so I said, "Let's get to it!" And we did.

It was raining, hard and cold so we had to make some slight adjustments to plans. Charley borrowed a cigar from his father's humidor and lit-it up on the gas stove in the kitchen. "We need to let it burn for a while and then it won't go out, even in the rain." Charley knew things. But Charley refused to wear a raincoat. "Of course not!" Charley never wore a raincoat. I knew that. Charley wears a Redskins stocking cap, black rubber boots and Winnie-the-Pooh pajamas, dressed as described, Charley grabbed the fuming cigar off of the stove-top and we left the Barretts' house and went out into the pouring October rain trailed by a thick plume of brown and black smoke. We would have time to air the place out and fix the lamp later. We stopped by our house next door where we borrowed two green camouflage water-proof tarps from our family's camping gear. We wrapped-up our bottle-rockets and cannon/radio-launchers in the tarps and scurried-off into the night, bent on ballistic retribution and bound for Finches' Run. The parents weren't due home until midnight. It was only 8:30. Everything was going according to plan... maybe even BETTER than according to plan! "Vengeance without judgement AND get paid! That's a trifecta!"

We kept to the gullies, back-roads and alleyways, avoiding traffic, crouching, sneaking, taking turns puffing on the cigar, keeping it lit for its big moment. We only had to travel about a half-mile to arrive at our destination, but because of the intensity of our evasive efforts we easily travelled twice as far. The rain continued, unrelenting. It was good cover. We marched on, crossed into Finches' Run and at last beheld the object of our devotions, the Finches' ancestral home, high on a hill and about to become condominiums and a golf-course,

We stayed off of the long driveway and kept to the trails and paths. We emerged from cover within the perimeter of mowed grass that surrounded the big, white frame house. The lights were on, and vehicles were parked outside. We put our tarps down within range of the house and Charley, Booboo and I lay down between them, Charley in the middle, puffing on the cigar. Booboo and I arranged our cannons and ordnance and got busy loading and aiming while Charley, alternating left and right, lit rocket fuses with the cigar. The plan was executed to perfection and an exploding fusillade enveloped the Finches' home on the hill, filling the air with light and sound and fury! We fired off all of our rockets and looked out in wonder from our camouflaged cover at the wafting proof of fifty-plus explosions. After the cacophony of the assault, the stillness was profound. I could almost hear the angels sing! It turned-out to be police sirens.

The first police car was upon us before we even had a chance to run, so we stayed-put between our camouflaged tarps, and they drove right on past us. It was pouring rain. The police parked in front of the house and ran up onto the front porch. Charley stuffed the burning-end of the half-smoked cigar into the mud. The sizzle made the cops on the porch look all around and shine their lights in our direction. We stayed still between the camo tarps, the front-door opened, and the cops went inside. We made our move.

We left everything where it lay and bolted back down-hill into the thicket towards the path that'd brung us. More cops were coming up the driveway. We ducked down and hid as best as we could, and it was just good enough and the second cop cruiser continued towards the Finches' ancestral home where the first two cops were back-out on the porch. Mr. Finch pointed our direction and hollered "THERE THEY ARE!" And we ran like rabbits down deeper into the thicket towards the bottom where the stream called Finches' Run runs under the road on the western edge of the property. The small stream, more a creek, passed underneath of Columbia Pike through a fifty-foot-long concrete tube culvert that also ran underneath a storage shed and lot built upon reclaimed earth. The concrete tube, too small for a large man to pass through, was constantly getting clogged-up. Kids could climb in, and we did, because it was a great hide-out, but I'd never passed all the way through, and never at night, and the stream was swollen with rainwater. I didn't see any other way. I could see flashing lights out on Columbia Pike and there were flashlight beams coming our way from directions. I led us into the culvert, and we crawled on our hands and knees against the current of the swollen creek. Charley was behind me, and Booboo was bringing-up the rear.

We made good progress and hurried towards the far-end of our escape underneath the western edge of Columbia Pike. The concrete culvert was relatively clear of debris and the water was manageable. But as we approached the far side we ran into a tangle of sticks. I began breaking them. Things were getting tight. I made a passage and pushed Charley and Booboo out in front of me. I had to take-off my raincoat to get past the sticks. The rubber jacket got wedged in the sticks and clogged-up the culvert downstream of us. The stream began to back-up and rise upstream of us. I pushed and pulled and dragged Charley and Booboo as the water continued to rise more and more rapidly. We finally had to duck our heads down and swim underwater through the last few feet of the culvert and all came-up bubbling and spewing, safe, outside the perimeter of the Finch property. I could hear a pack of search dogs barking and sniffing over on the far side of the culvert. The waters of Finches' Run continued to rise. We climbed out of the swelling creek and scurried-off up-stream into the woods separating the main road through town from the neighborhood and the elementary school that we attended. As we reached the path through the woods that led to our school, I looked back and saw that the creek was backed-up and cresting the roadbed. We fled down the path towards the school.

We heard the dogs again and kept running, avoiding streetlights and the police perimeter that extended for miles along Columbia Pike. We had to pass through Annandale, Falls Church and Lincolnia, detouring through a graveyard on Mount Holyoke. We tried several times to right our course and get back home but the police perimeter was a widely cast net and we had to retreat and reroute in the pouring rain and plunging temperatures many times. Charley never complained. He had even lost his rubber-boots and Redskins stocking cap. We walked and scurried and hid and ran in the rain for what seemed like hours and hours. At last, we found a way home, hopping several fences through an unknown neighborhood and burst through the Barrett's front door into the saving warmth of their foyer! We were filthy, freezing and soaked to the bone. The smell of burnt toast and cigar smoke hung in the air. Charley was careful not to step on the broken glass, but when his bare feet hit the beige carpet in the living room you could really see how badly they were bleeding. We would need some extra time to clean the bloodstains off of the carpet. I looked-up at the clock on the wall. It was 12:45 am. The Barretts walked in. "I'M SORRY WE'RE LATE! THE ROAD WAS

FLOODED!" gushed Mrs. Barrett. Then she stopped dead in her tracks and her chin hit her chest and that is where and this is when I shall pull the rope and draw the curtain of charity to close down this scene.

Postscript Analysis: To my knowledge, Charley never gave us up... unless he's written his own story by now, but I haven't heard of it. And even though the caper was, technically a success, and nobody got killed, according to plan, I still had to give the Barretts everything in my piggybank and my savings account AND mow their lawn for two-years to pay for the damages to the ceramic lamp, carpet, cook-book, kitchen ceiling and counter-top. I was also put on total restriction for six-months and to this day have not done any more baby-sitting for Charley Barrett or anybody else.

ELECTRIC FENCES

Evolution, even if you don't believe in it, is hinged on the ability of individuals to grow intellectually from their own nonlethal errors and of societies to get smarter from the terminal gaffes of their citizenry. And so, we humans, the very pinnacle of Natural Selection, are either the unchallenged superstars of learning from our foibles or the unmitigated masters of making mistakes. I strongly suspect, based on what I have seen, heard and personally endured, that we are more the latter than the former.

Women don't have electric fence stories. Extrapolated logically, this implies that women might be smarter than men. So, the fairer sex is probably smarter and definitely fairer than we menfolk. Therefore, because we know the Almighty to be inherently magnanimous in the dispensation of heavenly gifts, we can know with Divine certainty that the Y chromosome must be, by rights, in sole possession of SOME pillar of earthly grace. And that pillar, built by Y in the spirit of "why not?" would be the electric fence story.

Uncle Phil, like any Southern Virginia farmer worth his salt, was a certified do-it-your-selfer. He built, rebuilt, or added to every structure on the old family farm. Phil wasn't a professional carpenter, in that he wasn't proficient enough at woodworking to have outsiders pay him for the service, but he was good enough for doing what needed doing on the family homestead. He was a "country carpenter". This description of his tradesmanship covered his abilities as a plumber and electrician as well. And Uncle Phil, as necessity dictated, was not shy about learning from his mistakes.

A country carpenter opens and closes the first door that he's installed, notices where the door is sticking, adjusts the hinges or trims a corner, and makes adjustments to ensure that the next door installed won't be affected by the same hindrances. A country plumber can see which way the slop flows or if it flows at all and increases the angle of declination as flow demands. A country electrician, however, using Uncle Phil as a primary example, is up against a slightly different metric for success.

I helped Uncle Phil install the electric fence around the bull lot at the family farm one summer long ago. The electric fence installation was in response to the near constant destruction of the wooden fence that consistently failed to contain the boisterous bulls inside. The bull lot was in the field that separates the family home from the dairy and the newly installed breaker box for the electric fence was on top of a fence post along the gravel driveway connecting the house to the barn. Installation of the electric fence went pretty quickly compared to building and rebuilding the wooden one. And when the project was completed and Uncle Phil threw the breaker to the "on" position, it was just a little bit anticlimactic. No fireworks. No cheers from an adoring crowd. Just a dull "hum".

"I wonder if this thing is even working?" intoned Uncle Phil, foreshadowing the country electrician's slightly different metric for success. Phil grabbed ahold of the top wire of the new fence and his gnarled fist clamped down tightly upon it. Phil uttered not a word, but his clenched teeth were bared and rattling. His eyes went large and desperate.

"Is it working?" I asked Phil. He didn't speak but his eyes got even wider, and his bared teeth were chattering like a crate of milk bottles in a pickup bed on a bumpy road. I sensed trouble and it occurred to me to throw the newly installed breaker to the "off" position. When I did, Uncle Phil released his hold on the wire and slumped to the ground. "You okay, Uncle Phil?"

Phil didn't answer right away. And he didn't move much right away either. After a few moments he began blinking his eyes, unclenching his jaw, and rubbing his palm, which had a black burn mark across it. I helped Phil to his feet. "Fence works just fine," he said. "Let's go get some lunch."

If the X chromosome had been, in any way, involved in the learning experience thus described, then there's a good chance that the apex of this story's arc would have already been reached. But, the very next summer, I was shipped down to Vidalia, Georgia, to help Uncle Haywood Peacock with his hog farming enterprise, and Providence magnanimously provided me with a whole 'nuther opportunity to evolve.

Aunt Ethel met me at the train station and hugged me up real good, then drove us out to the hog farm, about an hour away. Uncle Haywood met us at the screen door of the front porch and greeted me just like always, handing me the 410-gauge shotgun along with two shells and saying, "Here ya go, Boy. Go rustle us up some lunch!" I dropped my bag, grabbed the gun, and was gone off the porch like a shot.

Grouse and quail were plentiful on the Peacock farm. I loaded a single shell into the small-bore shotgun and began intrepidly stalking prey. I crept through a corn field, across a creek bed and up to a fence line bordering a pine forest. It was an electric fence line. The fence was marked, and I found a place to climb a rock and safely step over it. What was not marked was the fact that this stand of pine trees was now Uncle Haywood's summertime hog lot. As I was keenly focused on tracking a fowl that I'd seen alight a little deeper in the woods before me, I didn't notice the thousand-pound sow and her gaggle of piglets until the sow jumped up and confronted me directly. The huge hog advanced on me, and I gave way. The sow was angry at the insolence of my intrusion and full-on charged me. I was wise enough to recognize the sow's advantage and backed-up in full retreat. However, I wasn't quite evolved enough to recall the exact location of the fence behind me and that's when the rubber met the road. Or more specifically, that's when the electric fence warmly greeted my backside. As I yelped and toppled backwards over the hot wire, I inadvertently squeezed off a shot from the .410. My errant shot went straight up in the air, scattering any potential game and alerting the Heavens of my Darwinian growth potentiality. I'm just lucky that I didn't accidentally shoot Uncle Haywood's prized sow, or I'd have been castrated along with receiving a black burn-stripe across the top of my buttocks.

When I dragged myself, defeated, back up on the Peacock's front porch, Uncle Haywood said, "I heard the shot. What'd you get?"

I sheepishly turned around and showed him my stripe.

"Oh," said Uncle Haywood. "I see. You got something more valuable than lunch."

"What's that?" I asked.

"An education."

An earthly education is only as useful as one's pursuits will allow. And in the throes of full-blown pubescence, all bets are off…

A scant few years after the burn stripe across my

buttocks which I'd earned down in Georgia had faded into memory, I was again back on the family farm in Southern Virginia for the Thanksgiving holidays. I was sixteen years old and jacked to the nines with testosterone. Uncle Phil told all of us cousins to jump in the back of the pickup for a ride down to the dairy to pick up a bucket of fresh milk. "I'll race ya!" I declared and took off running at an angle that bisected the farm, as Phil fired up the truck with the cousins in the bed and started along the gravel driveway.

"Watch out for the fence!" I could hear Phil holler out the truck's window. "And watch out for the bulls down there in the trees!"

I didn't pay him no mind. I was flying. It was the same electric fence that we'd installed several years before. Only the top wire was electrified. I climbed up and safely hopped over the top wire, unscathed, and hopped down into the bull lot, which looked empty at the time, and raced the wind across that lot like a Category 5 hurricane. The cold November breeze licked my face as the southern sun kissed my forehead. I was young and strong and running free! Then, out of the corner of my right eye, I noticed some movement down in the trees in the corner of the lot. Several young bulls emerged from the shade and began to give chase. I wasn't worried at that juncture, only exhilarated. I had a lead, the angle, and a plan. I tapped into my nearly limitless reserves and accelerated, running through the tall grass like an antelope out on the savannah. But the tall grass concealed a low spot in the bull lot and as I accelerated into the low spot I went down on my knees and continued running on my knees until my lead, angle and plan were vanquished and the bulls were barreling down upon me! By the time I regained my footing it was simply a mad dash for the fence line with no time for navigation and I could feel the bulls' hot breath on my neck as I clamored over the hot wire and received my stripes, severally, upon hands, chest, stomach and thighs.

While this tale might not have a clear moral, and although the trove of trials endured and related might not have gleaned an actual learning experience, per se; that moment, after my escape from the snorting bulls, shines forth from the clutter of my memories like a shining pearl. For, while some of us with the dented chromosomes, the very foot soldiers of the evolutionary process, lay panting and smoldering in the brown grass between the electric fence and the gravel driveway, others of us, like my less adventurous siblings and cousins, the very pinnacles of Natural Selection, are laughing like hyenas from the back of the truck. And, because we know that God created evolution, if a woman ever has a first-person electric fence story of her own to tell, then we can safely assume that evolution has reversed course and the Big Dipper is taking a personal day.

CUTTIN' WOOD

There is a healthy and robust relationship between math and wood. Carpentry is a good example of a profession where this in on display every day. The more learned in math the more proficient the carpenter. Every cut must be measured and marked. Understanding geometry plays a role in nearly every cut. Algebra is needed to estimate materials and labor. And one day, several years ago, I found out why I shouldn't have BS'd, lied and cheated through every higher math class after Algebra 1.

I had a small remodeling company and was hired to construct a large octagonal gazebo with a conical roof. "No problem." I thought, having neither built an octagon of any size nor nary a gazebo. But, trusting fully, without much empirical evidence, that I could trust my native skills, I used some Algebra and composed a winning bid. If my two-man crew and I could finish the project in three days, I would make a handsome profit.

The gazebo was a kit, and came with instructions, but every piece of lumber still needed to be measured and cut. And, because of the combination of the octagonal circumference and the conical peak of the roof at least one end of every single piece of wood framing required a compound miter cut where the cut has two angles. I had some experience with compound mitering doing crown molding installations and knew that it was more time consuming, especially figuring out the correct double angles. But the gazebo kit came with instructions, and I decided to read them. And here is where the rubber met the road with my carpentry career and my math skills.

As I stared down at the small black writing on the white paper of the instruction manual, and my crew stood there with their arms folded, waiting impatiently for instruction, it occurred to me that my high school higher math transgressions had finally come back to visit their shame upon me, for the key to the instruction manual, the key to unlock the mysteries of the gazebo project's multitudinous compound miter settings, was a single, simple logarithm. And to this day, all that I know about logarithms is that I didn't know what one was that day when I really needed to. The project wasn't finished in three days. I worked for three weeks in the hot sun, used twice as much material because I had to re-cut so many pieces of wood, and lost $37.50 for my efforts. And that's all that I know about logarithms. But I do know one thing about Calculus.

I found myself in a public library, picked-up the first volume that I saw and sat down to peruse it. "The History of Numbers." It turns out that Mankind, at some point long ago, began using similar sized and colored pebbles to represent family members and livestock. Bigger pebbles represented a handful of smaller ones. Then different colored pebbles replaced bigger pebbles and led to other innovations like Base Ten Math. And then we created math machines like the abacus, and we have created higher and higher forms of math. And that leads me directly to the question at the crux of this tirade. What do you suppose might be Latin for "pebbles?" You probably guessed it. Latin for pebbles is "Calculus." And that's all that I know about Calculus. But I do know one thing about geometry.

When I was ten or eleven years old, I got invited, for the first time, to ride with my father and his friends out to the country to cut down some trees for firewood. There were five grown men and me in three pickup trucks with multiple chainsaws and guns and plenty of gas, as well as two big coolers full of beer. We were looking for oak trees that were about ten inches in diameter. My father demonstrated for me how to use the chainsaw and safely cut down a tree. First, you need to find a suitable tree for your needs and identify a lane through the forest where your chosen tree can fall. Then, you cut a notch in the trunk down low on the side of the tree where you want it to fall. The notch should be more than a quarter of the diameter but no more than a third. Then you start cutting on the backside of the tree just above the top of the notch you cut on the fall side and when the tree starts falling you yell "Timber" and get the heck out of the way. My father and his friends found some prime specimens and felled several 8-10-inch-thick oaks. I helped and got some chain saw time and we cut up most of the trees into firewood length logs and then took a break.

My father and his friends were drinking beer. Budweiser was the undisputed king and they had two full coolers that they were working on. As we took our break, they were down to one cooler. A couple of men got out their pistols, set up some empty Budweiser cans, and began shooting. There wasn't anything for me to drink. No water. No nothing. I sucked on a couple of ice cubes until one of my father's friends, Fred Cox, said, "Awww. Let the boy have a beer. He's been working hard, too."

My father agreed and I jumped all over that. As far as my father knew that was my first can of beer and I acted like it was. And after I discreetly finished that first beer, I discreetly filched a second one and wandered about the outskirts of the wood camp as my father and friends laughed and drank and fired their pistols. And that's when I had a head-on collision with geometry.

I could see it plain as day. It was sitting there all along, a natural trinity. A trifecta. I didn't invent it any more than Pythagoras invented his theorem. I just noticed it, like Einstein noticed Relativity. I became transfixed as the angles of my calculations exposed the template of my theorem. I would fell three perfect 8-10 inch oak trees at once. I saw the lanes. They were only waiting for this moment to arrive.

Nobody stopped me as I picked up a chainsaw and walked towards the first tree of the trinity in my mind's eye. And nobody stopped shooting their pistols and drinking and laughing when I pulled the cord and started up the saw. I cut my forward notches in all three trees. All good so far. I made some final calculations so as to not walk into danger, took a deep breath and began my backside cuts. I made the cut on the third tree just as the first one hit the ground.

"THUD!" The ground shook with the impact.

My father screamed! "WHAT THE FU-CHRISTMAS!?" Only he didn't say Christmas.

When the second tree hit the ground, right on target, men started running around like disturbed termites, putting my theorem in jeopardy. As the third perfect tree fell, I noticed that my foolproof calculations were just a little off and it really was a miracle that nobody got killed. The third tree hit squarely on top of the remaining full beer cooler which exploded better than you could have ever imagined.

In the years that have followed, I've thought long and hard about that day. My father was madder at me than I've ever seen him. What did I learn? Well, my vision of the Trinity might not have been the right triangle. But, by putting my faith in math while cuttin' wood that day in the woods, long ago, I caused several grown men to get down on their knees and pray. And that's all that I know about geometry.

WHO NEEDS MEMORIES?

Common beliefs among us include the divine conjecture that when we are conceived and/or born, an immortal soul then inhabits our being and makes us something greater than the parts that went into it. I can buy into that theory. Knowing almost EVERYTHING, my immortal, relatively omniscient soul entered my virtually helpless baby body that was incapable of expressing any but the most basic of its needs. And, just as every being struggles at physical existence, the titanic effort to master my earthly vessel, in part, caused me to forget where I came from. Now that I have climbed the hill, crested it and gained terminal velocity on the down-hill slope, I am all but bereft of the memory of the furthest point of light from whence I was spawned. Until finally, memory has been removed from my rich trove of readily available literary crutches and I am free to contemplate all that remains, scars. And a fine way to get a scar, whether you are a precocious kid or a career diplomat, is to go back-packing on the Appalachian Trail.

In my early teens I began backpacking the Appalachian Trail with a friend from school. As we completed a few journeys, our goal became to pack lighter and more efficiently and hike further. On one particular journey, we were going to hike the mountain ridge that separates Clarke and Loudoun Counties. Our maps and advance intel indicated that there was a well-known trout stream that crossed our intended path more than once, and a river, the Shenandoah, down at the bottom of the mountain. Since Duncan and I were both experienced fishermen, we carried even less food than normal for a hike of similar length.

As soon as Duncan's mom dropped us off at an Appalachian Trail marker along the side of a mountain road and drove out of sight, we mixed up all of the water in our canteens with some orange Tang powder and some pilfered vodka. We drank a hearty toast and strutted off into the mountains like the Tin Man and the Scarecrow for a three-day hike with our canteens filled with screwdrivers, a couple of Zebco fishing rods, some trail mix and a couple of cans of pork and beans. We marched like storm troopin' gangsters for a couple of hours, straight up hill, and then took a little time-out for some more gangster Tang, which really seemed to refresh us. We continued our march up the mountain with renewed vigor, surrounded by deeper and deeper green. It can be disorienting to climb higher and higher and go deeper into the veld. As nightfall came swiftly upon us, we realized that we hadn't seen a trail marker in quite some time, so we stopped to consult our map.

"I think we're lost."

"I think I'm drunk."

Duncan dropped to his knees and puked. One look at his unearthly orange heave and I followed suit. Tang oblivion. I slept where I fell.

Day 2

The side of my face was embedded in a pillow of green. My neck, dangling awkwardly from the backpack still strapped to my torso, was bent at an uncomfortable angle. I sat up.

It was early morning in the Appalachians. Cool. Verdant. Aural. Fragrant. I slapped myself on the neck, too late to stop a biting fly. There was no immediate sign of Duncan. I staggered to my feet. My head was pounding. I looked all around me. There was still no sign of Duncan. I looked down at the lush flora bed-coat what'd just held my head, neck and face in embrace. Three ragged shiny leaves. It was poison ivy.

I forgot about the poison ivy as soon as I heard Duncan screaming as he came running from the thicket to the left of me! He dropped his backpack to gain speed. "RUUUUUUUUUUN!" he shrieked. He didn't have to tell me twice. Ground hornets! We crashed through the brush as the murderous little beasts stung us repeatedly. By the time they finally called off their assault we were even more lost and down two back-pack. Duncan got the worst of the hornets. I picked-up a bleeding scratch under my eye. We decided not to go back for our packs, so we were down to what we had in our canteens. Gangster Tang. We had some. Then I had an idea!

"Vodka has alcohol in it, right?"

"Right."

"And it's good to put alcohol on hornet stings and scratches, right?"

"Right!"

We both lathered up our stings and scratches with spiked Tang, and my wounds felt better instantly as the alcohol in the mixture soothed my skin with coolness as it evaporated. After the alcohol was completely evaporated all that was left on our skin was orange sugar residue. Biting flies love orange sugar residue and we were set upon like we were a flesh buffet. We had to keep moving, and fast.

Duncan pointed to the highest visible ridge and said, "We've got to get over that mountain." We started climbing.

Without back-packs or fishing gear weighing us down we were able to put some miles under our heels and steadily gained elevation. We didn't do a lot of talking. This was uphill, drunken, hungry hiking through virgin forests and over rocky outcroppings. By nightfall, we still had not summited the mountain ridge that we needed to get over and, once again, passed-out where we fell- hungry, thirsty, itchy, drunk, and exhausted. I drifted in and out of a restless sleep and had a vivid dream...

"The Raccoon Universe consumes all and then expels all and then consumes everything again. And the cycle repeats itself over billions and billions of Raccoon years, just as the Black Hole at the center of our galaxy recycles the stardust from whence we are formed. The bodily functions of the Raccoon Universe represent the expanding and contracting of this Physical Universe. The Great Raccoon Universe sits upon our collective chests until it squeezes the very life from each and every one of us, and we return, once again, to that black hole that spawned our stardust."...

I awoke from my vivid dream, slowly opened my eyes and met the yellow-orbed gaze of a raccoon, perched on my chest and admiring my breath. I could see that it was about to gnaw my lips off, so I gathered myself and jumped up screaming! One of the raccoon's claws ripped the flesh on the top of my right hand as I flung the pernicious little heathen 20 or so yards into the fen and thistle.

After my screaming and tossing of the bandit-eyed beast, Duncan and I were awake. It was nearly dawn, and we had no breakfast to eat, and no water, so we swigged the last of the loaded Tang and got back to climbing. We were getting pretty dehydrated and hungry, and it was a difficult climb. We finally attained the summit in the early afternoon and paused for a moment to take a good look around us at the mountains and valleys of the beautiful Blue Ridge panorama.

There was no trail or road or sign of civilization visible in any direction. We were contemplating our next move when we heard a roar! I looked up and saw a big, black mama bear standing up on her hind legs and bellowing at us from about 30 yards from where we stood! The big mama bear, trailed by two cubs, was in no mood for our company. She dropped down on all fours and started charging! We started running, downhill, and were soon catapulting and somersaulting down the steep, rocky slope, gaining momentum and narrowly avoiding maiming and/or certain death. The mama bear had no need to follow us down. We crashed and rolled for what seemed like days, breaking branches and ripping through thorns and thistle and a section of old, rusted barbed-wire fencing, bruising the stones with our bones, and picking-up an impressive assortment of sprains, fractures and scratches until finally coming to rest crumpled-up in the gravel on the shoulder of a mountain road-bed, where Duncan and I remained for quite some time, dinged-up and in a drunken, dehydrated daze, until summoned by the familiar honking of a car horn. It was my mother in our family station wagon!

Duncan and I limped to the wagon, piled in, and we

started back for home, stopping along the way for burgers and fries. We also made a stop at the emergency room where my mom called Duncan's mom to tell her about Duncan being in shock from the hornets and about his broken wrist. I received some stitches in my thigh after the doctor removed a piece of rusted barbed wire. And he put a few more sutures in the back of my head. I also received a tetanus shot, an IV with antibiotics, ointment for the poison ivy on my face and neck, and the first of several rabies shots because of the raccoon scratch on my hand.

Epilogue: Looking back, that hike in the woods was probably the least successful of our back-packing journeys. But because of it, I can see and touch enough of my knots and stripes to rest assured that I shall always be able to trace the arc of my foibles, even as memories may fade with time. For, who needs memories, when you can go back-packing on the Appalachian Trail?

KEITH PATTERSON

THIRSTY

I was alone and out of water, pedaling my beat-up road-bike in the high-desert badlands near the border of western Colorado and Utah. It had been 113 degrees Fahrenheit before sunrise that morning at the lone gas-station in the last town some fifty miles behind me to the east. The sun was directly over my head, and I figured it to be around noon. I'd lost my hat, my jacket and some other gear descending twenty miles in twenty minutes from Rabbit Ears Pass down into Steamboat Springs three days before. The oppressive heat that gripped me from the start of the days' ride had only increased and was beginning to feel deadly. I was looking for a town or a gas station or any sign of human life. I had already pedaled at least fifty miles so far that morning and at least ten miles since I'd swallowed my last drop of water. I was cramping from dehydration and let my bike drift to a stop in the middle of the baking blacktop.

I cupped my hands above my brow and scanned the unforgiving panorama, I could see for many miles in every direction. There was nothing moving anywhere. I had been counting heavily on there being a town right there where I was straddling my ten-speed in the middle of the road. "YOW!" Searing pain in my feet alerted me that the rubber soles of my shoes were melting! I shambled off of the oven-like asphalt onto the relative safety of the road's shoulder. I dropped my bike and hopped from foot to burning foot. I opened one pannier, took out my two books and placed them on the ground. I removed my melting shoes, and my socks came off with them. I had no replacements. I stood on the books to protect my bare feet from the scorched sandstone roadbed and with my left-foot set firmly on the Tao Te Ching and old King James protecting the heel of my right, I tried to catch my breath, clear my head, and assess my situation. I peered back down the road from whence I'd come. There was no sign of my cycling partner, Ted Aschenbrenner. He was carrying more water than me and I had gotten way out in front of him because of my lighter load.

After a month pedaling on the open road and several consecutive days laboring through the desert in drought conditions, Ted and I had figured-out that we each needed to carry an extra gallon of drinking-water, in addition to our clip-on water-bottles, to pedal forty miles. The first three days since we'd left the relative comforts of a KOA campground in Steamboat Springs, Colorado, we had found another town before running out of our water supplies. That morning, as we consulted Ted's map before embarking on the day's leg of our cross-country journey, Ted said. "There's no town for a hundred miles. I'm gonna carry two extra gallons of water with me today and you'd better do it too."

"Let me see that," I said.

Ted relinquished the worn, stained Colorado road map. We weren't sure if the road we were on was even on this map. "Dude, there's no town for a hundred miles," he repeated.

I scratched at the map and uncovered a dot on the grid about where we wanted to go.

"Dude, that's a piece of grease from the chicken wings we had in Steamboat Springs last week. That's no town. You better carry two gallons. I'm not sharing." Ted was serious. He tied down his two extra gallons of water, mounted his over-burdened ten-speed and wobbled off onto the black-top headed west with or without me. I made my decision concerning my supplies, tied-down, mounted-up and started-out pedaling after Ted, who was struggling with his two extra gallons of water one-hundred-yards ahead.

My decision to carry only one extra gallon paid early dividends as I was able to find a rhythm to my pedal-stroke and easily over-take Ted, who was understandably hampered. As I passed him by, Ted grumbled, "I'm not sharing my water. You better go back and get more."

"I'll save you a seat at the lunch counter," I replied as I pedaled by...

At least four hours and fifty miles had passed since I'd seen or spoken to Ted. I was out of water. Ted must have been at least twenty miles behind me because I could see that far and there was no Ted. And there was no lunch-counter, gas station or any other sign of comfort anywhere in sight. And not even a car or truck had passed by in several hours. And I couldn't just stand there, forever, on the side of that God-forsaken stretch of scorching blacktop, balanced in the burning sun between Lao Tsu and Saul of Tarsus.

"Ted must have stopped early for lunch," I surmised. I needed to make a decision. And it looked, to me, like I only had three choices. I could keep moving forward. I could go back from where I'd come, or I could stay put. I didn't have the energy to go anywhere without some water, shelter, and rest. I decided to stay put and wait for Ted or a passing car to save me.

I put my still-smoldering shoes back on and then noticed the ruined first course of an old block structure across the road, so I rolled my bike over and propped it up against the broken block. I took off my only shirt and stretched it over the frame of my bike and crouched down under it, leaning my bare back against the block as I sat on my books and attempted to piece together the decisions that had put me in this predicament…

The Aschenbrenner brothers, Ted and Dan, had planned and trained for this cross-country bike trip for months. I wasn't planning to go with them. I was holding down a regular job, working the 4 to 12 shift on the Railroad, at the motor pit behind Union Station in Washington, DC. During the day I was attending Northern Virginia Community College just across the Potomac River in Alexandria, where I rented an apartment. And midnight till dawn I was running the streets. I was showing off to some bad guys and my railroad bosses got wind of it. I realized that the bosses were with the bad guys. A deal gone south put me in several people's crosshairs had convinced me to leave the railroad mid-shift. That night I didn't sleep at my apartment. I slept in my van with my eyes open, parked deep in a residential neighborhood with multiple exits. At the break of dawn, I returned to my apartment, retrieved my bike and a few clothes, and drove over to the Aschenbrenner house. It was the day that they were leaving on their bike trip. They both said "Sure. Come on!" And off we went, from the waterfront of Alexandria, Virginia, headed west towards adventure and glory.

Skyline Drive and the Blue Ridge Mountains ruined Dan's right knee and we had to leave him in Radford, Virginia to recuperate. Ted and I continued west, grinding through Appalachia and out into the heartland, counting corn through Kansas and then conquering the Rocky Mountains in Northern Colorado. We summited Trail Ridge Pass and Rabbit Ears Pass, the tallest paved roads in the Continental United States and then cruised down from altitude into Steamboat Springs, Colorado where we met a pretty girl in a VW bus named Mona and got into a tussle in a cantina from which we were forcibly removed by some of the local gentry...

"WHOOOOOSH!" A pick-up truck drove right past where I was crouched under my makeshift shelter! I was so deep in my thoughts that I didn't hear it coming. I jumped-up and waved my arms and tried to yell! I could only croak. I felt skin on my lower-back tear-away stuck to the fossil concrete. Someone in the back of the passing truck yelled, "JERK!" and tossed off a couple of beer cans. I recognized his face and voice from the fracas in the saloon in Steamboat Springs a few nights back. I quit waving my arms as the truck bounced-off into the distance and walked my bike along the shoulder of the road towards the beer cans that were thrown from the back of the pick-up.

I tried not to get my hopes-up that the cans were full of cold beer. The two cans of PBR were empty except for scant warm backwash which I poured at my throat, and it wasn't enough liquid to pry my tongue off of the roof of my mouth. I blinked my squinted eyes and noticed a small cloud south of me up in the endless, pale blue sky.

The cloud was peculiar looking and left a trail that reached down to the horizon-line which was obscured by some scrub pines. "Smoke!" I looked down and noticed what could be a rough driveway that led down into a ravine and south into the scrub pine. Again, I carefully scanned both east and west. There was no

Ted and no traffic of any kind coming my way. It was time to make a decision, and it needed to be the right decision. My brain was feeling the effects of heat exhaustion and making good decisions would only get more difficult unless I found some water and shelter. I decided to follow the smoke and hoped that it was coming from a ranch-house cook fire and wasn't just a strange cloud.

The would-be driveway was rough, jagged, and uneven at best and might have been just a washed-out ravine. I had to walk my bike. The footing was treacherous and with every step that I took I was more convinced that Ted or a car or truck would pass me by while I kept on moving deeper into the depths of the rough scrub. The further away from the road I got the further away the smoke seemed to be. The ravine was rough, and I knew that my already damaged tires and un-trued rims were getting worse with every jolt and twisted turn. I considered reversing course with every difficult step, but I kept on trudging, further away from the paved road and deeper into the ravine. I lost count at two-thousand steps and then lost track of the wisp of smoke that I'd been following and became disoriented. My already desperate hopes went to a deeper place. A lone teardrop partially cleared one of my dust-choked eyes just enough and then I saw it, a small dirt-colored farmhouse with smoke coming out of the chimney, about thirty yards away!

I hustled towards my savior's humble mansion and

tried to call-out a welcome but all that came from my parched throat was a hoarse croak. I approached the front-porch of the house, leaned my bike against the corner-post, took two-steps as one and pounded on the front-door as politely as I could.

No answer. I pounded again, less politely.

Still no answer.

I was thirsty and I didn't knock again. I looked for a rock or something with which to break a window and get in the dwelling. Seeing nothing within reach, I thought of a suitable object and spun around to retrieve my tire-pump and came face-to-face with a double-barreled shotgun in the hands of a grizzled, filthy-looking rancher.

"WHAT THE HECK ARE YOU DOING OUT HERE?" he hollered.

"I... I," my voice was just a whisper. "I'm... bicycling... across... America! I'm out... of ... water..."

The leather-faced farmer looked me up and down in a flash of cold, blue eyes. "Well, you're crazier'n you look! Now get the heck off'a my porch!" The farmer waved that shotgun in my face. My grandfather had a gun just like it and I could tell that the gun wasn't cocked.

"Please, Sir," I pleaded. "I just need a small drink of

water… dish water… bath water… any water."

"BATH-WATER?" said the farmer sarcastically. Then his tone got deadly serious. "My cattle are dead and dying. My children have not had a bath in over a month It ain't rained yet this year. You ain't gettin' any water here, boy. Get it through your head. There's some water in the next town down the way. You look like you can make it another forty miles. Now get the heck off'a my porch and off'a my property." The rancher continued waving the barrel in my face.

I knew that the model of the shotgun whose barrel was two-feet from my nose was difficult to cock. I calculated the fraction-of-a-second that it would take the farmer to manipulate the double side-cocking hammer and prepared to make my move to snatch the gun and get some water… because I was thirsty. The farmer and I locked eyes. He saw what I was thinking and cocked the gun. I stopped calculating.

"You get the heck off'a my porch… NOW! I swear it… I'll bury you, boy."

I complied and backed-off the porch.

"Don't you even look at me, boy… and not one word, I swear it! I'll bury you!"

The rancher didn't have to tell me again. That model shotgun was difficult to cock but had a hair-trigger.

It was all up-hill as I hauled my bike back out to the

black-top from my fruit-less misadventure. I was beyond tears. I was beyond desperate. I was crushed, physically and emotionally. Each step was further than I thought that I could go. I found a low place that I hadn't noticed on the way in and stopped. There seemed to be moisture down in a crack too small for my hand. I reached in my pocket and retrieved one of my two pieces of folding money and stuffed the twenty-dollar note down into the crack to soak-up the moisture. That's when I heard the snake's rattle! I left my greenback imbedded in the crack and jumped out of that low place like a scared rabbit, dragging my bike unceremoniously behind me until I finally dragged myself back out to the baking pavement where the merciless sun was a little further to the west. I had forty-miles to pedal with the sun in my face and a headwind from the Northwest beginning to kick-up. I looked back towards the east and thought that I saw some movement...

Something was moving towards me at a leisurely pace from a great distance. Then it separated from the horizon and revealed itself to be a low-flying thing. As it got closer, I realized that it was many flying things. And then a flock of vultures flopped to the earth about a hundred and fifty yards away. I didn't like the looks of the creatures and there was no sign of Ted, so I got back on my beat-up road-bike and started pedaling.

It was a brutal slog. My body and brain, with deep-cuts to process and function, were forced to work independently of each other as I careened west towards the afternoon desert sun. I knew that I was down to two choices now. I could keep pedaling or stop to die. About every mile or three those buzzards would take to the air and flop about a half-a-mile ahead of me. I just kept pedaling.

Through the fog and misery of early-onset heat-stroke, my lizard-brain reflex took over and began to synch-up the rhythm of my body's various aches, cramps and injuries with the regular grindings of dust-clumped gears "Craing Cring Cring" and the droning bumping "wumpa-wap-wap... wumpa-wap-wap" of my badly bent front-rim. I could not open my mouth as my lips were stuck together. I could not really think because my fried brain-pain was shutting-down non-essentials. Random thoughts flew by like notecards in a tempest. The sun was in my eyes. My eyes were closed. I navigated by the shadows through my eyelids. My conscious mind was scorched clean of all pre-condition, and I stepped on through and glimpsed the dawning of this universe from the Singularity that followed the collapse of the universe before this one... "And when the Three Arrows of Time intersect at the Coming Singularity, Time = Consciousness. Consciousness x Energy, which is freed from equaling MC2 by the collapse of the Physical Universe = The Mind of God."

Beyond all thought patterns recognized by humans is the primordial response. Through the crust of my eyelids, I could see that the buzzards, lulled to sleep by the regular rhythms of my grinding monotony, failed to take flight as I approached broadside of them. I snatched my tire-pump and leaped from my wounded metal steed. I would bash the brains of the nearest vulture and bite a hole in his neck from which to drain its carcass of all useful fluids! As my feet hit the ground my weapon was raised above my head, and I was bent on mayhem! But my body would not respond to the instruction of its lizard over-lord and my cramped and depleted body crumpled down face-first into the dirt and scrabble. The buzzards, twenty yards away, didn't budge an inch. They had been here before.

I lay there for a long, hard moment. The surface temperature of the dirt in which my face rested was a little bit less scorching than I had expected. I lay there, with my face in the dirt, and cooled off for a long moment. When I finally raised my head up off of the ground, I caught glimpse of a green road sign about a half-mile up ahead. I slowly remounted my bike and struggled on. The sign came into focus. "Dinosaur, Utah, 10 miles."

You never really know what you can do until you have to do it. I had already pedaled at least eighty miles so far that brutally hot day, the last forty without water. I knew that I had another ten miles in me.

I rolled into Dinosaur five minutes before MacDonalds', the only restaurant in town, closed its doors for the night. I had one piece of folding money in my pocket and some change. $1.78 got me some fries and a coke and I was saved!

I maxed-out my free drink-refill quota before the staff asked me to leave so they could lock-up, then I ambled on over to the KOA campground just down the street. I could see Ted's bike but no Ted. I recognized a VW van parked next to Ted's bike. It was Mona's. She was the young woman that we'd met in Steamboat Springs several days before. Then it started raining, cold, hard rain, the first rain in six months. The camp-ground's bathroom door was locked, and I had given-up my tent the week before in order to carry extra water. So, I placed a piece of plastic over a picnic table and hunkered down. In between peals of thunder, I could hear Ted and Mona in the camper. It sounded like they were playing Yahtzee! I'm pretty sure that Mona was winning.

KARMA IN THE CAN

"To be human is to seek to rise above one's station. To evolve in thought and deed we must refuse and defy the stasis of mundane reality. But even the greatest of notions, like the sands of an hourglass, cannot escape the gravity of destiny."

In the third annum of my early twenties' California sojourn, I was on my way to work at Precious Preschool in Cupertino where I was the lead teacher, riding shotgun in Rodney's bastardized hybrid VW bus. Rodney, a self-taught VW mechanic, had borrowed the engine from my VW bus while rebuilding his. Thus, we were sharing a vehicle and I was late to work, again. We were coming down from the mountains east of Santa Cruz where we were residing at the Saratoga Springs State Park. Rodney, a mostly solid driver, had a self-soothing habit of weaving gently back and forth between the yellow lines. The flashing lights and blaring siren of a California Highway Patrol car alerted us to the fact that the officer behind us was not so gently soothed.

Rodney, a large man, was dangling his left meat-hook

out of the driver's side window as the CHP officer approached carefully with his hand on his holstered pistol. In Rodney's right hand was a Mason jar filled with incriminating substances which he handed to me as he whispered "Nate, sit on this for a minute."

I must have turned green as I attempted to conceal the damnable glass container in the seat behind my back.

"YOU DRINKIN'?" demanded the nervous patrol officer.

Rodney gave the officer a big, goofy grin and replied, "YOU BUYIN'?"

At that moment I knew for certain that I was going to jail.

There was a pregnant moment of uncertainty and then a felony intervened in our favor as a call came over the patrol car's radio. "Armed robbery in progress!"

The officer sneered at us through bared teeth and said, "Drive safely." Then he quickly retreated to his vehicle and sped off, leaving Rodney and I in shocked relief by the side of that mountain highway.

We continued down the mountain towards Precious Preschool until Rodney espied a red, VW bug, broken down on the side of the road. Before I could complain about being late, Rodney pulled over behind the bug, turned off the motor, grabbed his tool-bag and jumped-out to offer assistance. A kindly, middle-aged woman warily accepted his help and in minutes Rodney had replaced a fan belt and had her ready for the road.

"What can I do to repay you?" asked the grateful woman.

"We could use some work," replied Rodney.

"What kind of work do you do?" asked the woman.

"Nate here is a house painter," replied Rodney.

"It just so happens that our exterior needs painting," replied the woman. She wrote her name and phone number down on a piece of paper, handed it to Rodney and was gone.

"That's called 'Karma' baby!" said Rodney. "I wish it could always work out like this. We could put it in a can and sell it. Karma in the can!"

I made a mental note.

I was late for work that morning at Precious Preschool for the last time. But Rodney and I landed the job painting the exterior of the grateful woman's house and that money was enough to help us rebuild both of our vans and get me back home to Virginia where I somehow finished wrangling a degree out of George Mason University.

After graduation, the reality of the limits of the employment opportunities afforded me by a BA in

Psychology were quickly availed. I needed a big idea. Over several barley pops in a drinking establishment with a co-conspirator who found himself in a similar situation this big idea was unveiled. "Karma in a can!"

Michael Kidd, a recently graduated business major, wrote-up a prospectus, secured a sizable loan and became vice president of Karma in the Can, Inc.

We made up prototypes, decided on a design and sought a manufacturer. We decided to go for volume to keep the unit price down and ordered fifteen thousand cans before we had sold nary a one. We then dove, headfirst, into the deep waters of marketing our brilliant new product and were rebuffed by every gift shop in the region. We were trying to become the next Pet Rock. But trying to recapture that serendipity was beyond our pale. Then we caught a break. Ken Hakuta, who had sold millions of Wacky Wall Walkers in cereal boxes, contacted us about appearing at his Fad Fair in New York City. We gleefully signed on, bought our train tickets, got a hotel room, and lugged a couple of cases of Karma in the Can up to the Big Apple.

The Fad Fair had a 1st prize of $150,000.00 along with manufacturing, marketing, and distribution deals. I was Captain Karma, dressed in red tights and a purple cape, ready and willing to save the day with Karma in the Can. Michael and I almost pulled it off. It was a two-day affair and on the first day we sold all of our cans of karma, over 100 units. On the second day we faced the cameras and the judges. Michael and I did interviews with all of the major news stations and by the end of that day it was down to Karma in the Can and the Owie Wowie Girls for the top prize and immortality.

The Owie Wowie Girls were not only beautiful, but their product was also absolutely prescient. They owned the patent on putting cartoon characters on adhesive bandages. BLAMMO! There was no 2nd prize.

I had no time to change clothes, so I was dressed as Captain Karma for the train ride home from NYC. We drowned our disappointment in mixed drinks and by the time we arrived at Union Station we were blind drunk and at each other's throats. As we waited out in front of the station for our friend, Brian Addison, to pick us up, Michael and I got into a fistfight which attracted the attention of the station cops. I had a torn cape and Michael had a ripped suit as the Union Station Officers attempted to separate us. They were unsuccessful and at least two of them went down and got rolled at which point they called in the real cops. Several squad cars pulled up and we were quickly cuffed and sorted. Brian Addison pulled up just before we were to be stuffed into a squad car.

"Officers, please!" contended Brian. "You can't arrest Captain Karma." Brian was smooth as silk.

The officers looked at Brian like he was out of his mind. "These jokers are with YOU?"

"Yes officer. You have to excuse these men. They've had a very rough day, just now returning from a business trip to New York City where they've had their hopes and dreams dashed to bits. I'm here to take them home."

Somehow, against all odds, the officers un-cuffed Michael and I and released us into Brian's custody.

"You better take these idiots straight home," said the lead officer. "Do NOT stop anywhere in this city for another drink. If you do, and I catch you, you're ALL going to jail!"

"Yes, officer. Thank you, officers."

On the way home, after crossing back into Virginia by way of a couple of bars on M Street in Georgetown, we were pulled over by a state trooper. The trooper was a woman. Through the fog of my hazy vision, she looked marginally attractive. She asked Brian to exit the vehicle and as they discussed the situation by the front bumper I thought the trooper, being female, might appreciate a full body glimpse of Captain Karma. I got out of the car and prepared to wow her with my karmic insouciance. But before I could shut the car-door behind me or utter a sound, the peace officer spun me around, put her densely-heeled boot squarely in the crease of my red tights and deposited me unceremoniously into the back-seat of Brian's car. As she slammed the door behind me, and my stinging rear and torn cape slumped down into the upholstery I became vaguely aware of the gravity of my destiny. And Karma in the Can, Incorporated, the greatest of flawed notions, was, effectively, no more.

P.S. I do still have about forty cans left if anyone is interested.

The author dressed as Captain Karma.

KEITH PATTERSON

CRYSTAL'S

After a flame-out, a burn-out, a bike ride across the nation and a nearly two-year sojourn in southern California I returned home to Virginia and somehow finally managed to receive Bachelor of Arts degree in Psychology from George Mason University in May of nineteen hundred and eighty-five. I surveyed the landscape of job opportunities in my field afforded me an advantage by my hard-won diploma, at which point I decided to pawn my prettily painted piece of parchment puffery, along with the remnant of my Confederate folding money, for a pair of breasts for my boar hog. And being thusly equipped I launched upon a dual career as a house painter and professional musician.

I was a good house painter and customers told me so. I didn't receive as much praise for my singing, but I persevered and then one day had a little good fortune come my way. A friend from college, Ken Shubert, landed a job at a brand-new recording studio in Falls Church. Ken invited me in for some low budget demo work and we were joined in the studio of Cue Recording by some hot-licks local musicians and a producer, Tony Bonta, that liked what he was hearing. And at the end of our session, we had my greatest hit, Money Thang, which won in the Rap Division of the Mid-Atlantic Song Writing Contest and garnered some radio play on WHFS in Landover, Maryland. At that point I had some juice and some of our finest local musicians, including Tim Eyerman, Sean Peck and Charles Wright, offered their services for my low budget recording forays. I garnered more air-play on 'HFS, mostly because I'd pick-up Damian and Weasel at the bus stop down the hill from the station and play them my latest singles on cassette as I drove them slowly up the grade in my hand-painted VW bus. This repeated airplay and notoriety allowed me to assemble the finest group of soloists to ever grace a stage and to call them my band, Primal Virtue. If only the sum could have equaled the parts.

Primal Virtue was built to turn the beat around, with as many different time signatures in play as possible. One of our typical math rock constructs was for the rhythm section to play in 6/4, the guitar in ¾ with the trumpet and vocal in 4/4 time. Every 12 beats the whole band hit on the down beat. Even if we synched-up every twelve beats you couldn't possibly dance to it. But dance-ability was never even a concern of ours as we composed, rehearsed, performed, and recorded. We wanted to do what had never been done before. Dancing had been done before.

Primal Virtue consisted of Rafael Fernandez on guitar,

Teo Graca on bass, Peter Fraize on saxophone, Alex Krause on drums and yours truly, Rev. Nate on vocals. By sheer gall we gained some momentum as we played our way around the bar circuit. We did well in a battle of the bands and landed a showcase gig at Jaxx in Springfield, opening for The Tubes. Fee Waybill, their lead singer got sick in the dressing room before the show and The Tubes had to cancel. The Road Ducks, fresh off an opening slot touring with Molly Hatchet and Lynyrd Skynyrd, were recruited to open for us and we had our first and only headlining show at a real venue.

The show wasn't one of our best and the crowd that had come out to Jaxx for the classic southern rock of The Roadducks were in no mood for our odd-metered adventures and we never got invited back. We really believed that opening for The Tubes at Jaxx Nightclub was sure to be a high point launch up to another level of success but as we passed by the dressing room and loaded-out our gear the putrid waft of rock star vomit assured me that it would most certainly be a bit less than that.

We began to repeat the pattern of playing in the same bars around town. It was a little less thrilling the second time around. We were still playing the same twenty-three originals that we'd penned and recorded. Nobody had figured out how to dance to it, yet, but we did develop some loyal fans. One such enabler, Mark Lemmon, hired us to play his yard party. After our 3-

hour performance the crowd was less angry than most. We felt a resurgence of belief in our musical message. Mark suggested a gig in a bar that we hadn't yet played. The owner was a personal friend of Mark's and Primal Virtue landed a Friday night gig at Crystal's, a roadhouse on the eastern shoulder of Route 1 in Lorton, about a mile from the Penitentiary.

The chicken wire in-front of the band stand got my attention. So did the 6'8" 400lb biker/bouncer, Tiny. The microphone smelled worse than the dressing room at Jaxx after Fee got sick. The crowd was rowdy and was yelling for "Free Bird!" before we even got set up. The first half-empty beer bottle smashed into the chicken wire while we were still tuning our instruments. I looked over at Tiny, taking money and stamping hands at the front door. "I think they like you!" Tiny roared with laughter and then cut it short. "HEY, BACK IN LINE, ASSHOLE!"

The crowd grew restless. It was almost 9pm. "Y'all better start playing, NOW," said Tiny. "This crowd looks mean." Tiny looked concerned. I felt a lump grow in my throat.

I addressed the band. "Let's start with Ascending Half-step Sixes," I said.

"That oughta piss 'em off," dead-panned Teo.

"PLAY FREE BIRD!" Another beer bottle smashed against the chicken wire! The front door burst open, and some wild eyes and gold teeth came busting in!

"TINY!"

"SNAKE! WHERE YOU BEEN?"

"I JUST GOT OUT OF JAIL! YEEEEHA!"

It was a small comfort to know that SOMEBODY in the audience was happy. I counted us in. "ONE TWO THREE FOUR FIVE SIX…" The band lurched to life and the collective jaw of Crystal's patrons hit the sodden wooden floor.

"What the f--"

"THAT AINT FREE BIRD!" Several bottles hit the chicken wire! They were eye-level and maliciously intended. We played harder and faster in response to the open hostility. Women tried to line dance and were kicking each other's shins. We finished our first set faster than it had ever been played and paused to take a short break.

The crowd hated us not playing even worse than they hated our playing. Tiny glowered down upon us and said, "I don't think a break is a good idea, tonight. Keep playing."

I counted us in to Dancing with Grandma. It's in 5/8 and 6/8 with an intro in 17/8. The line dancers two-stepped until their shins were bruised and raw. The crowd got ever rowdier, and some mean drunks emerged. Tiny broke up fights and threw several men out into the street as we kept on playing at a furious pace. We went through every song that we knew. All three sets. It was only the end of the second set. The crowd was in a drunken lather. We started packing-up our gear. We didn't care about getting paid. We just wanted to get out with our lives.

"WHERE IN THE HELL DO Y'ALL THINK YOU'RE GOING?" Tiny roared as he blocked the door. "DON'T YOU WANT TO GET PAID?"

We looked at each other in disbelief. "That's still an option?"

"PLAY ANOTHER SET, DAMMIT! I'll have your check at 1:15." Tiny then turned his attentions to a past due patron and deposited him outside. We quickly set our gear back up.

"What can we play?"

"Let's play the first set again."

"They hated the first set."

The beer bottles were smashing into the chicken wire at increasing velocity and frequency.

"HURRY UP!" snarled Tiny, real desperation in his voice.

"What are we gonna do?"

We were in a spot. Time stood still like an

enchantment...

I pictured the scene in Deliverance where Burt Reynolds is lying in the boat with a compound leg fracture and a killer on the ridge above them and one of his surviving mate's bellows, "WHAT'RE WE GONNA DO, LEWIS?"

Burt grimaces, grabs his compatriot by the collar and groans, "Just... play... the game."

I was brought back from my revery by a full bottle of beer smashing into the chicken wire at eye level. I licked my lips and said, "Mmmm. PBR." The band laughed and the spell was broken.

"Anybody seen 'The Blues Brothers' movie?" I asked.

"Yeah."

"Sure."

"Anybody know Rawhide?"

"Maybe."

"Kind of."

Rafael picked out the "ding ding dingaling ding ding ding ding ding" intro and we were off and running.

"Move 'em out! Move 'em on. Move along! Keep those doggies movin'. Keep those doggies movin' Rawhide!"

We played Rawhide for forty-five straight minutes.

The line dancers got in step. Tiny brought us a round of beers with our check right after the show. As we loaded our gear into our van there was a fist-fighting, hair-pulling brawl in the parking lot. It was the line dancers, caught up in the moment. Tiny said that we could come back anytime. "Just gimme a call and we'll set something up."

Mercifully, Crystal's was bull-dozed before we could take Tiny up on his offer. And Primal Virtue, having peaked in that third set behind the chicken-wired stage, was thusly laid to rest soon thereafter.

SHORT RESUME

I WILL lie to you. Believe me. There's no use denying that gem. But, if you ask me if I'm lying to you, well, I would never lie to you about that. Because that would be a "bald faced" lie, and would constitute me stepping uncomfortably over the line of my social contract. I'm much more comfortable with "lies of omission", like at a job interview. My last job interview was ten years ago. I got the job. I worked at that job for ten years, and now, being recently retired from said job, and every other job, and being confident that I won't be applying for any more jobs in this lifetime, it seems safe to finally write down this story.

That last job interview, ten years ago, was to be a substitute teacher for a nearby County Public Schools system. My interviewer, a vice principal, made this comment as she looked at my resume. "This sure is a short resume for a man your age. And no real experience in this field." I could have offered up excuses. Or started making things up to fill in the gaps. Or, God forbid, I could've told the truth. But I really wanted this job, so I just smiled and replied, "Thank you." The vice principal stood up, excused herself, and said, "I'll be right back." She left the room, shut the door, and as I waited patiently for her return, I began daydreaming about a few lies of omission that were the real-life experiences in the service field I'd deemed best left bereft of a paper trail.

As a young man trying to graduate with a four-year college degree, I changed majors at least nine times. I attended four different institutions of higher learning in four different cities in two states on both coasts. I worked at numerous jobs and managed to stretch the process out to eight years. A few of the jobs that I held while attaining my higher learning involved working with the special-needs population. I didn't completely detest this form of work and finally decided on a Bachelor of Arts degree in Psychology as I planned to have a long career in service to others. While attending Grossmont Community College in east San Diego, I landed my first job in the service field. I was on my way.

This first job was a weekend gig. I was in-charge of a group home/halfway house for teenage boys who were transitioning from a mental institution. I was twenty-one years old, not particularly mature, and all alone in a two-hundred year old three-story Mission style edifice with a dozen psychotic teenagers for 36 straight hours, from 8pm on Friday evening until 8am Sunday morning. Before my first shift, I was given about 15 minutes of training, handed the keys to the drug safe, the front door and the safe room. And as my predecessor burned rubber fleeing the premises, so began my baptism.

These young men were a seriously disturbed group of individuals, in need of a lot of good, professional help. I wanted to help, but I was by no means a professional. I was a community college student with plenty of problems of my own. I was, at first, shocked by the baseline level of insanity on premises. Then it was med time. The whole crew lined up and gladly accepted the doses that I was dispensing. It was mostly Thorazine, and secondary drugs meant to counteract the negative side-effects of the Thorazine. These were heavy medications. And twenty minutes after dispensation, it was lights out slumbers for the whole gang. I locked the door to my private bedroom and tried to do the same. In the morning, before the crew had fully shaken their slumbers, it was med time again. Then breakfast and BOOM! The meds kicked in until late afternoon when their real personalities could shine through the anti-psychotic haze of their morning medications.

After a few weekends on the job, I began to make some progress in counselling some of these young men. We developed some rapport and maybe even a little trust. And then as soon as meds were dispensed, all progress slammed into a wall. The two scrawniest of my inmate charges seemed to be the most heavily affected by the heavy meds, and I began to suspect that these two smallest waifs were getting beaten up while passed out at night. Being a Libertarian, I decided to investigate and intervene in the name of what's best for freedom.

One Friday evening about three months into my employment, I arrived at the group home on-time and with a plan. I went directly to the drug closet and ritualistically prepared the evening meds for my charges. I flawlessly followed regular protocols, except for one part.

The Thorazine was in black capsules. Each of the young men received two black capsules, along with various other meds for their various individual conditions. I'd determined that each of the two scrawniest of the crew would get a half dose of Thorazine so they wouldn't be so vulnerable to nighttime abuse from the older, larger boys. I emptied two black capsules and refilled them with sugar from packets I'd brought from home. I used my bare hands to wipe away and scatter the Thorazine dust from the two capsules that I'd emptied and altered. It was a good plan, born of compassion and real concern for the well-being of the weakest and most vulnerable among us. In retrospect, among other things, I shouldn't have licked my fingers.

The evening meds had their usual effect on the boys. Nine o'clock and everybody headed off to bed. I felt a little sleepy and went to bed a bit early myself. I awoke groggily from a deep dark dream to the roar of police sirens! The sirens seemed to be coming from right outside in front of our building! I stumbled out of my room and down the hallway. Every bed was empty. I staggered outside into the glare and cacophony of police lights and sirens. A fire extinguisher exploded on the pavement nearby! Everybody was looking up. I did too. There, on the roof, in the middle of the night, fifty feet above our heads, were my entrusted charges. They were howling with glee! I pointed my finger and yelled "YOU GET DOWN FROM THERE!" They threw the other two fire extinguishers at me!

An officer approached me and asked "What's your relationship to these young men. I explained that I was in charge. And the officer said, "Come with me."

The owners and managers that ran the group home were soon on the premises. I explained exactly what had happened. I had nothing to hide. It was a good plan, born of compassion. I was escorted from the premises and told not to return...

I looked up from my memory. My interviewer, the vice principal, had not yet returned to the empty conference room where I sat alone. My thoughts drifted back to another job experience beneath pride of mention...

Three years after that debacle in San Diego, I was attending George Mason University and closing in on a degree while working for the county as a behavioral therapist. My first assignment for the county was working another weekend shift at a group home for consenting adults. When I arrived on Friday evenings I got the keys to a county station wagon, a hundred dollars cash for spending money, and a license to keep my clients entertained. All of the clients had their own money, too, and we went on many well-funded daylight excursions, including attending my friends, Ted and Caroline's, wedding. Ted and Caroline and their families didn't particularly appreciate our attendance THEN, but they're still married and still talk about the grand entrance that we made. My charges and I began venturing out at night and frequented local bars where we routinely cleared some dance floors. The clients loved me, and the bartenders recognized that our money was as green as everybody else's. Unfortunately, we ran into some county bosses one evening in a popular watering hole and I was relieved of THAT sweet gig. I wasn't fired, but I was placed on probation and given a little less responsibility. I became the Roving Counsellor and worked the vacation shifts of different employees in every group home in the county. This allowed me to become acquainted with all of residents of all thirteen affiliated group homes in the system, as I documented interactions and behaviors and got familiar with their strengths, weaknesses, skills, talents, and interests.

Among these residential clients were artists, musicians, savants, and athletes. Each of them sufficiently impaired, mentally and/or physically, to require their inclusions in the county group home system special needs community. One day, while chasing down an escapee, it occurred to me that there were actually several pretty good athletes among the two-hundred and fifty or so residents of the thirteen group homes in my orbit. And it seemed to me that we could all use some more exercise, so I hatched an idea that seemed utterly brilliant at the time. "A softball league for the residential clients!"

Every group home supervisor loved the idea and claimed that it was their idea, up until a certain date. On that date it was roundly decided that it was MY idea. That date is the focal-point of this vignette. We decided on a big field next to a newer group home with a big kitchen, wrote up some rosters based on a typical athletic draft, and assembled four "dream teams". We would play two three-inning semifinals before lunch, and then a three-inning championship in the afternoon. The families of all of the Residential Clients in our special-needs softball league were invited. Lifetime memories were going to be made.

The top half of the first inning stretched on out into the late mid-morning. Not only would The League not play both semifinals before lunch, but there was serious doubt that we'd complete the first inning before nightfall. That all changed with one swing of the bat. CRACK! A slow roller approached second base and stopped short of the makeshift base-path. First contact of the day. Half of the entire four-team client league began screaming instructions. Everybody else just stood there. Finally, after an interminable spasm of raucous instruction, a client-athlete near the resting softball bent down, picked up the ball and bolted straight out towards center field. She did not stop to consult her teammates or coaches and seemed to pick up speed as she bounded into the woods at the edge of the big field. This client-athlete was one of our better runners. Several coach-counsellors, myself in the lead, gave chase. Every ambulatory citizen of the system gave chase. Several electric wheelchairs headed full-speed for the exits.

It was after dark before we rounded everybody up. At 9pm, there was only one client-athlete still unaccounted for. I found him standing behind a tree near a first-floor window in a residential neighborhood. The police gave us a ride to the station where our superiors were notified, and a car dispatched. The supervisor that was sent to the station, after securing the prodigal client-athlete in the rear of the county vehicle, informed me that the League had folded and my employment was no longer required, and I shouldn't use them as a reference. And I could find my own way home from the police station...

The assistant principal conducting my interview to be a substitute teacher for the county school system reentered the room where I was reminiscing. "Mr. Patterson, sorry that took so long."

"Uh, no problem."

"I just have a few more questions."

"Sure," I said. I shook off my daydream and tried to look competent. I choked back a sneeze until air escaped from the inside corners of my eyeball slits.

"Mr. Patterson, it says here that you worked for twenty years in home improvements. Is this true?"

"Um. Yes."

"Well, do you have any references from those twenty years of home improvement work?"

In that moment, the only jobs, contractors, sub-contractors, homeowners, and various clients that I could recall were in situations that had gone south. "Sure I do. Plenty... of references." I just sat there and smiled. Her move.

My interviewer shuffled papers and left again. "I'll be right back," she said over her shoulder. I drifted back into my daydream and thought of a home improvement references that I couldn't use...

One spring, my House Doctor co-physician, Roderick, and I were painting the exterior of a big, white, wood sided home. It had a lot of peeling paint and damaged wood, and we offered a very competitive price for the repairs and preparations. We would make our dime on the finish coat. 25 gallons of gloss white. Oil base. We would spray. Roderick and I each had a sprayer and were both considered to be spray masters. The weather was clear all week. We finished the prep, including replacing rotten wood trim and siding, scraping loose paint, sanding rough edges, caulking cracks, re-glazing windowpane mullions and priming all bare siding and trim, and arrived on Friday morning with a fool-proof and well-worn plan to start on opposite sides of the house and meet in the middle. We were tried and true. Battle tested in the operating rooms of residential opinion. We were the frickin' House Doctors, booted up and ready to wail in double Graco Rack IV glory. We wore respirator masks and goggles. We had spray shields and had all of the bushes and flowers covered with tarps and plastic. There was only one extenuating circumstance that could possibly affect our roll. The 17-year Eastern Cicada Brood X.

Billions of cicadas were supposed to crawl up out of the ground and make a whole lot of racket and a big mess. Nobody knew exactly when they were gonna show up. Or if they were gonna show up at all. It seemed like more of a "suburban legend" anyway.

"Let's do this!" barked Roderick as he climbed his ladder.

"ARRRRRRG!" I roared through my respirator. And we dove into our work like seasoned spray professionals.

We sprayed like beasts for six straight hours in the drying sun without a hitch or drip and laid on all 25 gallons. Two full coats. We touched up the ladder marks behind us as we went. Perfection! We cleaned our sprayers with paint thinner and cleaned up all of the plastic and drop-cloths. We left the jobsite content in the knowledge that we had done our very best.

The 17-year Eastern Cicada Brood X were equally convinced of our skilled brilliance and showed up later that night to get a closer look.

When Roderick and I arrived Saturday morning to touch-up and get paid, we were greeted by at least 17 million cicadas stuck all over the sticky white gloss oil base paint. All 4 sides of the big house. 17 million. They were still alive and beating their wings like the Damned! We should have just walked away. We tried to fix it…

My interviewer returned to the meeting room. "Mr. Patterson, I have some good news. You're hired."

I worked for the county school system as a substitute teacher for nine years. I started off working in elementary schools. As I became more self-assured and gained some confidence I began subbing in middle school. Then I moved up to high schools and stayed in one particular school for the entirety of my final year of service, when and where I believe that I finally learned the key to being a successful substitute teacher. It is not up to me to be funny. And I'm not being paid to entertain. It is enough to be competent and fair and helpful. But before that crucial realization came to light, I made enough mistakes in judgement in my substitute teaching career to confirm that after nine long years, my resume is even shorter than it was when I began. Believe me.

SILENCE

There are many different virtues of every stripe that can be mined in pursuit of polishing up your humanistic resume. And which of these positive personality traits are most useful in trumpeting one's own inherent decency has always been a matter for debate. "Master, what is the greatest of all the virtues?" asked the devotee. "Is it patience? Piety? Long suffering? Devotion? Kindness? Empathy? Filial love? Bravery? Or steadfastness?"

Without hesitation, the gentle master resolutely answered the question posed by his disciple. "The greatest of all virtues is love." Within a week of this declaration the devotee had cut off the ear of a Roman guard and was in jail awaiting trial and the gentle master got sold-out for a fistful of silver dollars and strung-up in a former tree and left to die. So, being that Love is trickier than it might at first seem to be, I am now endeavoring to pad my prospectus with virtues that might yield more tangibly predictable results. And as I get older and wiser and stay married to my second wife, Kelli, longer and longer, I believe that my experience coupled with my remaining intellect has helped me identify the virtue that could possibly pay the biggest dividends once it is mastered. Silence.

I picture silence as the most powerful locomotive in the train yard, its greatness defined by near limitless potentiality, at rest in the muffled beauty of gently falling snow. Silence is the greatest of all the virtues because of all of the other virtues that you've got to pull off to get it done. To hold your tongue in the heat of argument or even in polite conversation requires patience, steadfastness, and strength. To keep from scrunching up your nose and saying more with your facial expression than words ever could takes physical and emotional control, as well as empathy, caring and commitment. Recently, my wife and I were engaged in an after-dinner conversation. She was telling me a sad story that I'd heard before and I was listening intently. At least, I was trying to listen intently, or at least portray that I was listening intently. I did this out of love, and self-preservation. I had been mastering all of the virtues for well over an hour and a half, and my wife and I were near the end of our second bottle of Merlot. But alack, the track of my wife's sad recollection, that I'd already heard before, stretched out into the future, and still had no end in sight.

"Sunny and I first met when I was training with Steven Shmertz of Darlingdale Stables over in Loudoun County. Nobody could ride Sunny but me, so we had a special bond from day one," continued Kelli. "Trixie Barrowfield, Steve's partner, used to groom for Penny

Winklestreet, of the Kent Town Winklestreets, who go back seventeen generations of Pennsylvanian show hunter champions and that's where I met Darlene and Ernst, who you met at Nelly Murphy's engagement party for her daughter, Winnie."

I nodded affirmatively like I was following along. "Darlene and I have been riding together since Pony Club. I was always the better jumper rider, but Darlene was always better at dressage. Darlene met Ernst in Girl Scouts. I'm pretty sure he's gay. We used to all go out disco dancing when we were travelling up and down the east coast with the horse show circuit and sometimes Ernst would borrow one of my dresses and put on some mascara before we went out."

I was nodding agreeably while secretly mastering at least seventy virtues and keeping a straight face. I'd heard all of this before. But, blame it on the Merlot, something about this telling of the tale just hit me funny. I was thinking "So Ernst is a cross-dresser and Darlene is good at dressage. So, is Ernst better at "cross dressage"? But I didn't say it. I bit my purple tongue and honored the greatest of virtues with mastery of them all. And as I poured the last of the second bottle of Merlot into our glasses, I braced for where I knew that my wife's story was destined to go.

"Darlene and Ernst really loved Sunny because they knew how much Sunny loved me. And after that asshole groom hit Sunny in the head with a chain for attacking the pizza delivery guy, Darlene and Ernst were so supportive of me for learning how to competitively jump on a horse with one eye. I will always love them both for that."

I'm listening and nodding and sipping Merlot. In my head all I can hear is the old tune "I'm riding through the desert on a horse with no name" with the new lyric "I'm jumping in a show on a horse with one eye." But I did NOT burst into song. I bit my lip.

"Sunny could only approach jumps from the left, but he was so quick that he could make up for any lost time. We won our qualifying jumper class and represented our region in the Washington International Horse Show."

There was a moment of silence, the first in quite some time. I instantly overplayed my hand.

"That's a really big deal, isn't it?" I knew that it was a big deal. Kelli knew that I knew that it was a big deal.

Kelli looked at me like I was a moron. "It's only the biggest and most important show on the circuit." She wiped a tear from her cheek, took a sip of wine and got to the saddest part of her story.

"On the morning of the third day of the show, while Sunny and I took a little break from warming up and practicing on the jumping course, Sunny turned his head around to look at me. He had to turn his head a long way around because of his bad eye. But I'll never forget the look that he gave me." Kelli was brushing back tears. "It was like he was telling me that this would be our last show together. This would be our biggest ride and maybe our last." Kelli was openly crying. "We took third place out of seventy horses and riders. It was the absolute pinnacle of my riding career. Sunny was dead within a month. I really thought that he would be my forever three-foot-six horse."

Silence. I strained against an overwhelming tide to keep it thus. "Three-foot-six horse." I knew what that meant. That's the minimum height of the jumps in the division that Kelli and Sunny competed in. There is nothing inherently funny about "three foot six". It's a standard of the English Jumping School. But, of course, with my mind's eye all I can see is a tiny horse. Silence. It is the pause between universes. The possibilities are limitless, but there's only one way that this is gonna go. And I totally ignored the heartfelt needs of my weeping, grieving wife, my better half, my lover, and best friend. I had been listening intently and I should have continued listening intently. But the bait was too enticing, and instead of remaining silently vigilant to the needs of my one true love, I fired up the monstrous engine of heartless shtick masquerading as my soul and tooted my own horn as the silence train roared to life and left the station.

"Those Brits," I said casually," they seem obsessed with three-foot-six."

Kelli looked over at me. She was snuffling. "What do you mean?" she asked. She was completely sincere.

Vulnerable. Needing me to be kind, truthful, attentive, and understanding. I, on the other hand, had identified my mark and fully committed to my bit.

"It might just be a coincidence, but three-foot-six is also the official minimum height for a dwarf in the ancient English sport of Dwarf Tossing."

"Really?"

The most important person in my world was asking for the truth. And what I had was a Monty Python skit rattling around in my head. It was the scene in the movie 'Time Bandits' when the towering John Cleese, playing Robin Hood, bends down to interrogate the band of time travelling dwarfs that have dropped in on him and his merry men. Cue the English accents...

"And how long have YOU been a robber?" asks Robin Hood.

"Four-foot-one, Sir," answers the dwarf...

"Where did you hear that?" asked Kelli.

"That's common knowledge in the sporting world, my dear. If you kept up with the sports section, you'd know these things."

Silence.

I should have stopped my charade right then and there and never mentioned it again. Fat chance.

"Three-foot-six is the minimum height in dwarf tossing," I continued, before shifting to a Pythonesque Sherwood Forest lilt for the capper. "The maximum height is 'four-foot-one, Sir.'"

Kelli got the reference. We've seen the movie together more than once. She did not, however, laugh. I laughed. Like a braying jackass. Kelli put her face down in her arms, burst into fresh tears and sobbed as if she'd been wounded. I knew what I had done.

"I am such an asshole."

Sobbing Silence… Kelli slowly gathered herself and looked up at me. "It's just who you are. It's who you've always been."

Silence… What she said was true. It hurt. I took it in, bowed my head, closed my eyes, relaxed my shoulders, and resigned myself to the facts. "I am an asshole, with mastery of no virtues at all. There are no shillings in my heavenly accounts less the outright gifts of my betters. I have routinely put my need to make myself laugh above the needs of others. I am a narcissist."

Silence…

I opened my eyes and beheld the beautiful face of my loving wife. I could see that she was still hurt by my callousness to her emotions. But, Kelli really loves me. She knows me and loves me better than anyone ever has. I saw a little bit of hope flicker in her soft, dark eyes. So, I tried to explain my thought processes and the genius of my tomfoolery complete with playing the parts and delivering the lines of both John Cleese as Robin Hood and the time bandit dwarf that he's interrogating. "Four foot one? Yes. That IS a long time, now isn't it?" It was arguably my greatest performance of all time.

My wife got up from the table and walked away.

Silence...

Loving someone that already loves you shouldn't even be considered a virtue. We've all got to do better than that to make any positive change in the way that we treat each other. Showing someone that already loves you that you love them should be the easiest thing that there is. I have even messed THAT up.

Fortunately, learning from mistakes has ever been my sole educational option. And, in simultaneously rejecting Pride while accepting the truth of my own ignorance, I can, without hypocrisy, advise the reader to, "Do as I say and not as I do". And though I remain in no position to make declarations concerning my own growth of countenance, I compel you all to behold and embrace the great engine, asleep on the tracks in the falling snow. We all know its name and color. It is Golden. That mightiest and most monstrous of locomotives. Do not EVER let it leave the station...

Silence.

SALIM'S PLACE

Recently, an emporium of collectibles that sells my original paintings attained a rare piece of a stone antiquity. It looks to be of Asian origin but was acquired from the estate of a recently deceased U.S. army officer who pillaged in Asia as well as in Europe, during and after the World Wars. I was enthralled with the piece and ended up trading one of my paintings for the 5'4' tall 600-pound statue of a beautiful goddess. She didn't, yet, have a name, that I know of. But I went ahead and mortared the ancient sculpture to a concrete footer in a nook at the top of the Boar's Rock at Frampton Head, in the Donkey Run, right here at our own Kastle Keep Farm in Berryville, Virginia.

The stone goddess is a water bearer. She holds a bowl, tilted 90 degrees, pouring forth blessings upon all before her. I kneeled down on the slope and got in the path of her bowl of blessings and let that wash all over me. I asked the Powers of the Universe to watch over us as we travelled. And to watch over all of our critters and fur babies. One of our barn cats, a black male feral named Dodger, rubbed-up against the back of my leg. A fuzzy blessing. And a power move by a male feral.

Dodger touched his paw to my exposed ankle. We both knew that he could slash me and be gone before I could reach him. I exhaled serenely, and let Dodger be the first to move. When he retracted his paw from my ankle, I got-up slowly and went to meet Kelli in the barn.

I, myself, personally identify as a donkey person who explains everything to the cat, and my wife, Kelli, an avowed dog person, tends to explain everything to the horse. And that was the very last and most important thing that she and I were doing in the barn on that cold Thursday afternoon in January right before we left Kastle Keep Farm and drove to Dulles International for our flight to Paris.

"Lulu, you be brave. You are big. You are strong. And you are important." It was Kelli's standard line when explaining our travel plans to the horse.

We were about to go out of town for a spell. And all of the barnyard coterie instantly knew exactly what was going on as soon as Kelli began complimenting Lulu for no apparent reason. It was written all over their furry faces. "Your father and I are going back to Paris for four days and three nights. Connie Broyhill will barn-sit again while we're away. You all remember Connie, don't you?"

The horse, donkeys, cats and dogs all uttered positives as they rolled their eyes. Their expressions said, "As if you need to ask?"

Willa, the barn cat, was sitting in my lap, as per usual, while we were discussing travel plans in the barn aisle. What was different was I wasn't wearing my thick, leather barn pants because I was dressed to catch a plane. Willa reacted to an unnamed movement and sprang from my lap! Her barn cat claws easily pierced my cotton trousers and shirt and dug into my right thigh and chest. It only felt like a couple of scratches. And we had a flight to catch. So, we finished our goodbyes and left our precious little farm for a foreign adventure. I would look at my cat scratches when we got to our hotel in Paris.

It was a long flight. We were fighting a headwind and several time-zones. It was a direct flight to De Gaulle International and the flight-crew was French. So, I had to show-off my 2 years of college French, especially to one tight-skirted flight attendant, who paid me no heed. But Kelli paid me some heed and chucked me in the ribs before I was about to say something else that was unnecessary.

We watched some movies and videos and listened to some music as the massive Boeing 767, slicing through mild turbulence, careened towards our destination at fifty-thousand feet. We were fed a decent meal from rattling food carts. Kelli and I each had a glass of wine and we talked for a long while. We were both feeling tired and tried to get some sleep. About mid-way across the Atlantic, I started feeling warm and sweaty while my throat began to feel kind of scratchy and dry.

I grabbed my medicine bag, told Kelli where I was going, and got up to go to the water closet.

It was an over-night flight, and most all of the passengers were sleeping. There was no line at the water closer. I cleaned and dressed the cat scratches on my thigh, took some Benadryl and ibuprofen and returned to my seat. "You alright" Kelli asked me as I sat down beside her. I had the aisle seat. "Yeah, I'm fine," I replied.

"Let's try and get some more sleep," Kelli said groggily as she leaned her head on my shoulder. In seconds she was gently snoring. Several times I cleared my throat to suppress a cough. I took a throat lozenge from my pocket, unwrapped it and popped it into my mouth. It helped to soothe my throat. I tried to relax, ignoring the turbulence, and let Kelli sleep as I tried to do the same.

We arrived at De Gaulle International before dawn to begin our four-day three-night Paris trip. And then caught the train to the Gare du Nord station, a major hub, where everything was temporarily shut down because of a bombing at the station in Brussels, only a couple of hours away by train. The French police, both men and women, were lean and serious, wearing body armor and wearing AR-15 assault weapons, triggers in-hand. They were looking for the bombers in stations all around the European Union who were still at-large. The passengers in the station were all cool and collected, like they'd done this drill a few times before.

After the armed sweep of the station, we were allowed to leave Gare du Nord and catch our train to the Port Royal station. All told, it was only about a twenty-minute delay.

The subway ride from Gare du Nord to Port Royal Station was uneventful, though I was giving everybody the side-eye without actually staring directly AT anybody. As far as we knew, the Brussels bombers were still at-large. We sat near some locals and listened to their conversations, parsing their rapid-fire French as best as we could. I put another throat lozenge in my mouth just before we disembarked at the Port Royal Station. Then Kelli and I ascended two flights of stairs with our roller-bags and carry-ons and emerged at street level on the Boulevard de Port Royal, at the eastern edge of storied Montparnasse and, hopefully, not too far from our destination, an Air B n' B in an old apartment block named Passage D'Enfer. Our rental wouldn't be ready for a couple of hours, so we decided to kill some time inside of a tiny patisserie, one block east of the Port Royal Station, to have our breakfast and consult our Left Bank street-map.

The small shop was in a much older building that was wedged between two federal-style block buildings on either flank. The proprietor of the small bakery and café, Jean Eric, spoke even less English than we spoke French, but he was agreeable, so we parked our bags against the wall at our backs and sat down at a low, communal table, where we looked at a small menu and ordered breakfast. I chose a slice of quiche. Kelli got a croissant. And we both had a cup of coffee. Jean Eric was engaging and seemed to appreciate our attempts to speak French.

A couple came into the patisserie and sat down at our shared table. I thought that I had seen them earlier that morning at the Gare du Nord train station after we'd arrived from the airport. They parked their roller bags, dark blue like our own, right next to ours and spoke to Jean Eric in hushed tones. They ordered without a menu and were served immediately. We were served shortly thereafter. Kelli and I spread out our map of the Left Bank while Jean Eric continued conversing with the other couple.

"This is the main drag in this part of town," Kelli said as she pointed to her right. "This way is west, and this road is called Boulevard Du Montparnasse." She then gestured to her left, "If we go east this same road is called Boulevard De Port Royal. If we turn left out of this shop and then make another left one block down, we walk a quarter mile and enter Les Jardin Du Luxembourg from the south end. And if we make a right turn out of this shop, we walk a half mile, turn left and we are two blocks from our rental."

"Cool," I replied.

Suddenly, Jean Eric's eyes opened large as his nose twitched in the air. He abruptly quit his conversation, spun around on his heels, threw his hands in the air and shouted, "Mon Dieu! Mes croissants!" He then bolted down the steep narrow stone stairs at the back of the shop into a rising cloud of belching black smoke, bellowing what I knew must be every swear phrase in the local dialect that I'd ever need.

Jean Eric did not immediately return from his scorched ovens down below. The couple who came in after us dropped some Euros on the table, took two roller-bags and left. A steady stream of expletives continued emanating from the fuming pit. We tallied our meal, put our money on the table, grabbed our bags and left the smoke-filled interior of Jean Eric's shop for the crisp, cold air of the street. We still had an hour and a half before check-in at the rental, so we decided to walk the neighborhood and get our shoes scuffed by some real Parisian cobbles.

We continued west on Boulevard Du Montparnasse, past where we would turn left at Avenue D'Enfer to get to our flat, crossed over the broad boulevard at a crossing light a few blocks down and entered into Le Cimetiere Du Montparnasse from the north end. I was immediately staggered by the immense weight of human history on and under these pediments and monuments. The told and remembered a quantum fraction of the unsaid multitudes who lived and died and were buried in and under this place, the Left Bank of the mighty Seine.

The original city/state of Paris was centered on the biggest island in the middle of the Seine, the Isle de la

Cite, where now sits the storied and magnificent Cathedral of Notre Dame. It is a natural fortification, possibly the oldest continuously inhabited piece of property on this earth. Long before the Cathedral was ever conceived, Paris was synonymous with the Isle de la Cite. As the city of Paris grew out from the Isle de la Cite, and early maps were drawn, the Seine was oriented vertically, up and down, instead of left-to-right coinciding with east-to-west like most modern maps. So, the Right Bank of the Seine was across the river to the north. The Right Bank became known for its' architecture and institutions. The beautiful and durable limestone that built the Right Bank was mostly mined from the rich mineral deposits of the Left Bank, south of the river. This arrangement fueled the steady growth of the world's greatest city for two-thousand years.

Parisians, known to be flamboyant in many ways, are remarkably practical in others. As the centuries passed, and the minions by the millions lived and died in the great city, the proper cemeteries were filled to over-flowing. It was a huge problem. And the rich stone deposits of the Left Bank were played out. So, it became common practice to back-fill abandoned mines with the unwelcome dead. The original Montparnasse, of which only parts are still visible, was built upon millions of corpses encased in rooms of extracted limestone. Many centuries of largely unregulated mining, building and development led to a large-scale collapse of much of the area's foundations back in the early 1700s. Thousands of cellars and basements were flooded with corpses. The City of Light has a dark underbelly.

Kelli and I toured the Cemetery for a while, paying particular attention to the war dead and famous artists and authors and then exited through the south gate back onto the streets of Montparnasse, where a cold wind picked-up and chilled our faces. We put our heads down and marched, dragging our roller bags behind us. My roller bag felt like it was dragging and seemed a little bit heavier than I thought it should. I figured one of the wheels was going bad but I didn't think anything more of it right then. The road we were walking along had no clear markings or signage and seemed to be drifting off to the south. The sun wasn't visible on this gray morning and our map suddenly seemed useless. Kelli and I stood side by side and looked all around us, really taking it in.

Many buildings and monuments in many parts of Paris are at least a thousand years old. The blending of old to ancient to modern, at least with what architecture is visible above ground, is a thing of wonder. We walk a few blocks lined with apartments and office buildings from two-hundred years ago. These are the new buildings. Turn a corner and a modern building is being erected, a crane that can reach-up ten stories is parked upon cobblestones that are fourteen-hundred years old. Next door is a stone wall and staircase down to who knows where and a brass plaque with the date 471 AD. For a moment, there on the street somewhere in southern Montparnasse, standing in the cold morning wind, I felt like Kelli and I could have lived there during any period of history. We held hands. I leaned-in and kissed her cold, red lips. "Welcome to Paris, Lover," I said. "Which way to the B and B?"

Kelli let go of my hand, held our map with two hands and studied it. "I think we crossed off of the grid right here," she explained as she pointed at the southern edge of the map.

We worked our way west, turning left and then right as we walked the blocks that seemed to be running northeast and southwest. "I think we should work our way back north now," said Kelli, while pointing directly at Federal style apartment block.

"We'll have to zigzag."

My roller bag was dragging. It seemed heavier than when I'd woken up that morning. In six blocks we bore left, ten o'clock, onto Boulevard de Port Royal. At an intersection we crossed over Avenue Denfert-Rochereau. There, on the corner, was an ordinary edifice with a small bit of signage in carved stone that read "Les Catacombs du Paris." It looked like a bar on U Street in DC. I hadn't realized that the Catacombs was so close to where we were staying. There was a line beginning to queue along the block wall in front. "You want to tour the Catacombs while we're here?"

asked Kelli.

"No way," I replied. We consulted our map, confirmed our directions and put our heads down. The cold breeze was picking up. A few more blocks and we turned left on Avenue D'Enfer, stopped into a small grocery for some food, drink and supplies and arrived at our rental just after check-in time. 3 Passage D'Enfer.

It was a third-floor flat. The apartment block dates back to the early 1800s. The staircases were narrow and built of ancient hardwoods with hand-wrought iron railings. The apartment was small and efficient. The bed felt nice.

"Let's go for a walk in the Luxembourg Gardens after we eat a little lunch," said Kelli.

"Let's do it," I agreed, though I would've preferred a short nap. I took my Benadryl and ibuprofen and we sat down to lunch.

Lunch was pate, cheese, and bread. We thought it might be prudent and we drank water with this first meal and then hit the streets of Montparnasse, headed north towards the southern gates of the Luxembourg Gardens.

Les Jardin Du Luxembourg is the Central Park of the Left Bank. The Gardens host a daily throng of Parisians and tourists, walking, exercising, playing tennis, sailing miniature sailboats on the reflecting pool, buying and selling, hustling, haggling and just touring.

The bronze and stone monuments and statuary are stunningly epic. The gardens, even in early spring, are gorgeously lush and meticulously sculptured. Kelli and I kept to the central walking thoroughfare and continued towards the northern gate, about a mile away. Just before the gate, to the right, is the Medici Fountain, its' mantel piece a thirty—five-foot high bronze casting of the Gates of Hell, commissioned by Catherine de Medici in the sixteenth century, to complete and compliment her Palais Du Luxembourg, which resides impressively on the left side of the northern gate, between the reflecting pool and the Rue de Vaugirard. The northern half of the enormous edifice is Le Senate, the very seat of power in France. The 16th century's grandest castle was well-guarded by crack troops and hyper vigilant dogs. The northern gates of Les Jardin Du Luxembourg, fifty yards to the east, bore a constant flow of human foot traffic, unimpeded. We walked around the sidewalk in front of the Senate building, crossed over to the north side of Rue de Vaugirard and started walking down-hill on a cobblestoned street.

"How far to the river?" I asked Kelli.

"About a mile. You feel like walking that far?"

"Let's do it. It's downhill from here."

"It's uphill all the way back to the flat," said Kelli.

I felt pretty good at that point. "I want to see the Seine,

today," I said. "It's our first day in Paris, and I want to kiss you on the Bridge of Locks and Chains."

We walked down the aged cobbles, passing shops of every kind, every few blocks a modern pharmacie in a building that could be four-hundred or fourteen-hundred years old. Art galleries, cafes, dress shops, men's shops. And then, we were forced to turn either right or straight. We went straight, and down. Then we came to left or right and I think we went right. And then we were suddenly in an alleyway that felt ancient even by Parisian standards. The cobbles were ancient. Beautifully irregular. The alley opened-up into a dim courtyard square, fifty meters each on two sides, and a bit more or less on the others. All sides of the square were angled and uneven. It occurred to me that this place looked as if it hadn't changed in a thousand years. It felt cold and damp and had no visible exit except for a narrow stone stairwell down under a dry-stacked stone wall. We were standing between two statues framing the entrance of a bar. The statues were identical, except one was covered in moss and lichens. The bar was closed. The dusty, peeling painted sign above the door said "Chez Salim". There were people around. Shadowy figures. Running fast, almost flying. A busker playing a flute, crazy good. A man selling smoked meat over an open fire. Mean children cornering a stray dog. Danger lurked. My neck felt hot. I looked inside the window of the closed bar. The bar was empty... but no, I thought I saw someone in the back! I wiped the dust off of the front window and peered inside. I got a glimpse of three men except for three men dressed in eighteenth century clothes sitting around a table in the back. Their table was roped-off and had a sign that read "Reserve". I rubbed my eyes, and the men were gone. The Reserve sign was swaying as if just disturbed. Kelli grabbed my arm and dragged me back the way we'd come, up and out of the dank, deserted courtyard. As we emerged upon familiar cobbles, Kelli felt my cheek and said, "You feel hot, Sweetie."

She was right. I could feel the heat in my body. I tried to play it down. We were on vacation in Paris. "I'll be fine," I said.

We walked the last two blocks to the river, hand-in-hand. We crossed the Rue De Seine and walked out over the footbridge named the Bridge of Locks and Chains, where lovers have chained and locked mementos and lockets onto the wrought-iron mesh and rails of the footbridge for many decades. I had a lock and chain and we attached it to the bridge. I put a throat lozenge in my mouth, and we stopped and kissed and held each other and looked into each other's eyes, and I tried not to cough while kissing my beautiful bride. "I love you, Kelli."

"Awwwww. I love you, too, Boo." Kelli is a great hugger.

"You are really starting to feel feverish," said Kelli. "Let's get you back to the flat and get some hot tea and honey."

I didn't need to answer. She kissed my cheek, put her arm around mine, and we started walking.

We crossed back over the Rue De Seine and tried to find the same street to return, back up the grade towards Le Senat and the Luxembourg Gardens. We weren't even close and ended up off-course by a couple of miles. I was getting cold, tired, and hungry, and darkness was closing in. We found ourselves in an old section of Saint Germaine Du Pris, where Ernest Hemingway, the author, had once lived in a water-less flat with his first wife, Danny. We had to consult our map a few times, but we adjusted course a few more times than that and eventually ran into what we hoped was the western wall of the Luxembourg Gardens. We made a right. And even though it took a little longer than we'd hoped, we were able to orient ourselves in this strange and wonderful city, on the Left Bank, after dark, and drag ourselves back to our warm, cozy flat at 3 Passage D'Enfer.

We ate a light dinner. It was the same fare as lunch, pate, cheese and bread. This time with a glass of inexpensive French Bordeaux. The wine was wonderful. We took showers and I did my medicines and treated the cat scratches on my thigh, which seemed to be healing. Kelli showered first and by the time I was through in the bathroom, Kelli was asleep. I was exhausted and climbed under the covers beside her.

As Kelli slumbered gently beside me, the wind picked-up and it began to rain. Not a deluge, but a continuous patter. It was a lovely sound, but it did not put me to sleep. I felt exhausted. My throat had moved on from scratchy to full-on sore. My nose was running AND stuffy. I was coughing. Kelli kept-on snoozing away as the rain and wind kept-up their patter and clamor. Sleep would not find me.

I tossed and turned and tried to get comfortable. My stuffed-up nose turned me into a mouth-breather. I imagined the antihistamines having an effect and clearing my sinuses. I struggled to master my condition and finally, I began to relax... to breathe slowly and deeply. My nasal passages began to open, and I was laying there, in bed, in Paris with my wife Kelli, breathing softly and listening to the rain. And sleep still would not come to me. I could hear the clock on the wall ticking. I could hear my own heart beating, the wind blowing, the rain falling. Then I heard voices out in the courtyard below our window. I hoped that whoever it was would quit talking or move along, but the conversation did not desist. Then I could hear four distinctly different voices, down in the courtyard, in the wind and the rain, arguing. I got up out of bed, careful not to tug on the duvet that Kelli and I shared. She kept on snoozing contentedly.

I pulled back the drape and looked out of the window of our third floor flat. My vision was blurred by the rain and the condensation on the windowpanes, but I could make out four figures below me in the courtyard. As their arguments continued, in French, I realized that I could understand it. There was no time to ponder WHY I could understand this conversation in fluent French. One of the men turned towards me and looked-up. We made eye contact and he spoke to me. "Kennard, we need your help."

"Please help us."

"Please."

So, these four strangers needed my help, and I needed them to stop yelling outside of our window in the middle of the night. Calling me "Kennard" didn't bother me as much. I quickly and quietly got dressed, left Kelli sleeping, exited the flat and went down to the courtyard to see if we could work things out. It just seemed like the thing to do.

I opened-up the heavy, iron front door of the apartment block and stepped-out into the gently falling rain. Four men stood before me, wearing clothes that looked like they belonged in the 1700s. The men seemed like they belonged in an era different from the tale that their clothes told. It occurred to me that maybe they got a flat tire on the way home from a costume party.

"Gentlemen, please," I said. "We are trying to get some sleep."

The oldest of the men said that they were only trying

to get some rest, as well.

"How can I assist you so that we can all get some sleep?" I asked.

All three men started talking at once. They were not happy and needed separation from each other but were also like brothers, united in their commitment to the general betterment, but bitterly divided about how to get things done. "These guys obviously have some history together," I remember thinking.

They needed me. My participation was required in whatever they had going on. And these gentleman in period duds wanted me to come with them. For a split second they had me. I was listening to my inner boy scout, ready to help some older people. Then I shook it off. It was raining. I was feeling a little bit feverish. I didn't know these guys. "Look, fellas. Come into the foyer here, and get out of the rain for a minute," I said. "Lemme call you a cab."

"Oh no!"

"We won't come inside this place!"

"Not here!"

"Not the Passage through Hell!"

"Fine. Suit yourselves," I said. "I'm going back upstairs and try to get some sleep. I don't feel well. Goodnight."

As I shut the big iron door, I could hear the men

protesting my decision. "Get some sleep yourselves," I said.

After the door clanged shut, I heard the heavy-set man say, "If we don't get any rest, you won't get any sleep!"

"Bullshit." I was at least going to try.

When the big, iron door clanged shut I was engulfed in darkness. The corridor off of the foyer leading to the staircase was narrower, and the floor rougher, than I'd remembered. I heard voices, muffled and clear. Voices other than the strangers in the courtyard. There was laughter and crying and a scream. I thought I heard what could have been a gunshot! But it was far away… and I couldn't be sure. There were passages and stairwells leading down, hewn from stone and rock, that I hadn't noticed before. I could feel my heart-rate and blood-pressure increase. I found our staircase, climbed the three flights to our rented flat and returned to bed. Kelli was still sleeping, slumbering softly beneath the covers. I carefully crawled in beside her, struggling not to wake her.

The rain and wind continued. Every now and again I'd get comfortable, then I'd hear the voices from the courtyard. I began to cough. I had to extricate myself from the covers to go to the bathroom. I did a round of Benadryl and ibuprofen and a gargle with Listerine. Then I put some Vaseline on the cat scratches on my thighs, took a leak, drank some water and went back to bed. On the way back to the bed I looked out of the window, down into the courtyard. I saw no one and heard no voices. I crawled back under the covers as stealth itself. Kelli kept sleeping. I got comfortable. I began to breathe deeply, and I could feel my deep breathing getting in synch with Kelli's. The wind abated but the rain continued pattering gently on the roof and sills. I could hear the same voices in the courtyard. "Damn them! Those inconsiderate assholes." I was livid. I tried to control my breathing through my stuffy nose and lower my heartrate. Relax. Gentle rain. Assholes out in the courtyard talking. "Damn!" An infernal cycle continued without cessation... until Kelli stirred and stretched, greeting the new day that was peeping through the window.

"Good morning, Darling," said Kelli.

"Good morning, Boo."

"Did you get some sleep? I sure did."

"Not really," I replied. I don't think I slept a wink.

"Oh, I'm sorry, Boo. I know you're not feeling well. It looks like it's going to be a nice day. The rain stopped. We might even see some sunshine."

"Where are we going today?" I asked.

"Let's walk west towards the Montparnasse Tower," she said, more than ready for me to ask that very question. "Then we'll head north towards the theater district," she continued. And then we'll walk back down to the river and tour the Musee d'Orsay."

Resistance was futile. "Let's do it," I said.

We made our preparations. I took my medications. Kelli checked the local weather on the TV. We had some sliced apples and yogurt for breakfast and hit the streets. I noticed the faint aroma of cooked meat as Kelli and I passed through the foyer, where we parked our roller-bags and hung our coats. I didn't think any more about it right then and we left the flat. The meat smell didn't smell bad. It's just that it was unexpected. I figured it was just neighbors cooking-up something delicious.

We made the decision to forego the bus pass and walk our way around the Left Bank. We wanted to feel it in our bones and know it intimately. Walking on cobblestones for eight hours will sort you out in this regard. We headed west on Boulevard du Montparnasse and followed it to the Tower du Montparnasse, the most despised building in Paris, other than the crystal pyramid at the entrance of The Louvre. We navigated north, found Rue Gaite and located the restaurant that Kelli's friend had suggested Le Pedant Ivre. We had a wonderful lunch at a heated outdoor table, across from the theatre, and a gang of actors on Vespas. Then set out to find Boulevard Saint Germain and followed the historic street to within two blocks of the Musee d'Orsay.

We had a full day of witnessing and studying a

blinding array of stunning art. Several days isn't enough to fully take in just this one magnificent museum. There was an exhibit that was Monet's private collection of art by other artists. Cezannes and a Picasso next to a Manet and a Matisse. Some, like Manet, apply layers of light that overcome the darkness. Others, like Matisse, only cover the light that was always there. Some are color theorists. Others, students of shadow and brightness. Then there was Van Gogh. Layers of paint, technique defined by trance-like commitment. Canvasses defined as much by the paint that he removed as by what was applied. Genius at critical mass. And, as Kelli and I stood in the midst of this absolutely brilliant collection of these great works by my favorite artists, it was the Matisse that really floored me.

We toured until dark. Then we dragged ourselves back uphill along Boulevard Saint Germain, southeast towards Les Jardin Du Luxembourg. We were getting familiar with the map and oriented well enough to find the eastern wall. We followed the wall until we recognized our neighborhood, where we found a café a few blocks from our flat and were seated at a table on the heated terrace. We ordered from the simple menu. We enjoyed a couple of glasses of smooth white wine with a hearty meal of baked chicken, potatoes, and green beans.

After our meal, Kelli and I had a leisurely walk back to 3 Passage D'Enfer, three blocks away. We took showers. I did a round of my medications. We watched some French TV and went to bed. We were both exhausted. We had walked at least ten miles and toured a museum that day. Kelli fell asleep on my shoulder.

I lay on my back. My throat was sore. I could feel my pulse pounding in my forehead. Kelli rolled off of my shoulder and fell asleep. I tried to control my breathing and heartrate and had some success. The Benadryl kicked-in and my sinuses began to clear. I could feel myself relaxing. I had already missed one night's sleep. I was exhausted. I wasn't coughing for a moment. I was drifting towards temporal oblivion… I heard familiar voices down in the courtyard outside of our window. I said to myself. "Those bastards!" I was not going to give in to these assholes.

I rolled and I tumbled the whole night long. Couldn't catch a wink. I had to get up several times because of coughing and congestion and taking my medications and using the toilet. And every time I would crawl back into bed and started to get comfortable, I would hear the damnable conversation down in the courtyard again! And again! I was really getting tired, and irritated. And I did not feel well. But I stuck to my guns and did not go to the window to encourage the Four Velveteers. I figured that it was just a matter of time before they found something else to do. I crawled back into bed. Kelli was still sleeping. I began to get comfortable.

"Good morning, Darling," said Kelli, softly and sweetly, sunlight creeping through the bedroom window. "Did you sleep well?"

It truly amazed me how my wife's sweet, simple inquiry could sound so cruel. "I slept a little," I lied. "Where are we going today?"

Kelli had a plan, of course, and had done her research. "There's no need for the heavy boots and the long underwear. I checked the local weather, and it looks like fifty degrees and sunshine."

Our heavy boots and long underwear are what we kept in my roller bag. We hadn't even needed to open it since our arrival.

"So, let's walk through the Luxembourg Gardens and stay straight after we leave the north gate in front of the Senate," she explained. "No matter which road we take, north of Le Senat, it will intersect with Rue Saint Sulpice, where we'll make a left. And we'll run right into St. Sulpice Cathedral. I'd like to do a quick tour, then continue west on Rue de Grenelle, which will lead us to within a block of the Musee Rodin. We'll do a quick tour and then it's only about a mile to the Eiffel Tower. I've heard that there are lots of great restaurants in that area. We'll have a late lunch."

"Quick tour?" I said to myself. I knew that this was going to be a long day. I didn't really feel much worse than when we'd arrived. But I didn't feel any better, either.

"Sounds good," I said.

We made our preparations, had a quick breakfast of bread, fruit and cheese and then launched. On the way out the door, as we passed through the foyer, I noticed the meaty odor again. A little stronger than before. Cooked red meat. It didn't seem like an emergency at that moment. "Probably the neighbors." So off we went.

Our third day in the most beautiful city on earth went almost exactly as Kelli had planned. The Cathedral of St. Sulpice, the Musee Rodin and the Eiffel Tower are all wondrous far beyond the limits of the thin veil of my literacy. But, apart from the magnificent histories told in marble, granite, paint, bronze and steel, there is a humbler history of equal gravitas, right under the soles of our shoes. The mighty cobblestone.

Different eras produced different sized and shaped stones, some dating back to the Romans. And every era of devastation and renewal is written in the tapestry of their laying. In times of conflict, ordinary citizens pulled the stones from the streets and used them as weapons and barricades. More than a few invading armies had their skulls crushed from above as they paraded the Parisian streets. Beautiful, useful, and deadly. And you better have some sensible shoes if you're going to walk on them all day long.

We arrived back at the flat well after dark. I was beyond exhausted. It was our last night in Paris. Kelli put her hand on my cheek. "You're burning up," she said. "Take some ibuprofen and I'll make us some dinner. Then we're putting you to bed."

We had a simple dinner. I wanted to be romantic, but I really felt like crap as we lay down on the bed and got under the duvet. Kelli fell asleep quickly. She has a gift.

I tried to regulate my breathing, to breathe through my nose instead of my mouth. Relax every muscle as a conscious decision. I was so absolutely exhausted that I'd completely forgotten what I had to know was about to happen… I heard the voices down in the courtyard.

I extricated myself from the duvet without waking Kelli and went to the window. I could see the same four men in velvet breeches that had been robbing me of sleep for three straight nights. "Kennard, please. We need your help."

Looking back, it was almost as if I was in a trance or something. I left Kelli sleeping, put on my cap and jacket, let myself out of the third-floor flat and descended the two flights of the spiral wrought-iron staircase down to the ground-level corridor. I opened the big iron door to the courtyard and stepped out into the cold, night air.

"Thank you so much for helping us, Kennard."

"Wait a minute," I said. "I didn't say that I was going

to help you. I just want you to move the conversation away from under my window, so I can get some sleep. You look like reasonable men."

"Kennard, this matter concerns you," said the heavy-set man. "The Gatekeeper sent us to bring you to him."

Looking back, there were probably a few more questions I should have asked before deciding to leave my sleeping wife and go off into the night with four strangers to see the "Gatekeeper". But I was exhausted, badly in need of sleep. And these men seemed sincere. And they were obviously relentless. My defenses weakened. "So, what's this all about?" I asked. "And… Who ARE you guys? And… why do you keep calling me 'Kennard'?"

"Come with us," answered the older man. "We will answer your questions along the way."

Seemed reasonable at the time.

We headed north towards the Port Royal Station, but there was no train station where I thought there would be one.

The first to introduce himself was a charismatic individual named Danton. He looked just like Jack Black. His expressive eyebrows and demonic grin implied chaos. He seemed pretty straight-up to me. Then a bearded man with glasses introduced himself as Dr. La Voisier. He mentioned a few of his degrees and discoveries and sounded very self-important. I wasn't sure that I liked him. A heavy-set gentleman said that his name was Robespierre. He gave me a quick speech about the "poverty of liberty" before he was cut-off mid-bullshit by the older, baldest gentleman, who introduced himself as Voltaire. I thought I was looking at Robert Downey Jr. with male pattern baldness and long, gray hair. He said that he was a writer. I instinctively liked Voltaire. He seemed to be the leader of the culottes crew.

We entered a low building close to where I thought the Port Royal station to be. It seemed to be a multi-purpose dwelling and included a barn and a small bakery. We took a stone stairwell down. Then we took another. I tried to stay oriented east to west, but I quickly lost it. As we travelled along a corridor, the four men tried to tell me, while interrupting each other and starting fresh quarrels amongst themselves, why I needed to go see the Gatekeeper. Voltaire, in between a lot of eyeball-rolling at his arguing compatriots, explained that during the Great French Revolution, Danton, Robespierre and Lavoisier, the finest French democratic minds of their age, began bickering and back-stabbing amongst themselves until all three lost their heads, literally. They were all beheaded by guillotine and their bodies were interned to the already overflowing cemeteries of Montparnasse.

We were in a long chamber sloping down. I was disoriented but imagined that we were heading north towards the River Seine.

While Danton, Robespierre, and Lavoisier kept-up their bickering, Voltaire told me that after the collapse of the foundations of old Montparnasse, a huge rebuilding effort created the Catacombs of Paris, where over six-million sets of skulls and femurs that had flooded the basements of Montparnasse were neatly stacked and catalogued. It was a monumental task and has been the life's work of one man in-particular. And we were about to meet him.

We entered into a cavernous intersection of many corridors, all lined with neatly stacked human skulls and bones. There was an enormous half-round desk and a big, bearded, and bespectacled man behind the desk with his back to the wall. There was a queue in front of the big desk moving to and from and in all directions. All points led to the big desk. The queue moved quickly. It was our turn. On the big desk was nameplate. It read "Gatekeeper- Well of Souls." Voltaire spoke first, "Here he is, Sir."

"I can see that," curtly responded the Gatekeeper.

"Do you know why you are here, Kennard?" asked the Gatekeeper.

"Not really," I replied, honestly. "I just know that if I can help these guys get some rest, maybe I'll be able to get some sleep, myself. They would not leave me alone until I agreed to help them. But I really don't know how I'm supposed to do that."

The Gatekeeper at the Well of Souls looked down on me from his Big Desk. "Kennard, I manage the remains of over six-million Souls. And these four fools are the most irritating of them all."

Robespierre, Danton, and Lavoisier began grumbling and scuffling their buckled shoes.

Voltaire just shook his head and rolled his eyes.

"They claim that I mixed-up their remains," explained the Gatekeeper. "And maybe so. But I have no time for their petty quarrels, and I am tired of their bitching. These men could have changed the world but chose, instead, to cut-off each other's heads! Idiots! Kennard, I cannot thank-you enough for doing this work. If you can sort-out these fools' femurs and skulls, then they will be able to rest, and you and I, as well. And only when all of those who are restless are satisfied will I be able to leave this desk. You are helping ME."

"W-w-well," I stammered. "You're welc--"

"Oh, and there IS something that you can do for ME along the way," continued the Gatekeeper. "In fact, I INSIST!"

I didn't like the sound of the Gatekeeper's voice

My crew all looked down at their buckled shoes.

I was thinking, "Oh shit. Here it comes..."

"I want you to go to Salim's Place," said the

Gatekeeper.

"Salim's Place." I thought I'd seen it or heard of it.

"And bring these knuckleheads with you, said the Gatekeeper, nodding towards the grumblers and the eye-roller. "Maybe they can help you. Maybe not. Tell Salim what I want."

"What do you want?" I asked.

"Tell Salim to challenge Hemingway and Picasso to a contest, one against the other. I want Hemingway, the writer, to make a piece of art. And I want Picasso, the artist, to write a poem. I want the winner chosen by the patrons' applause. And I want to know the results of the contest and the reactions of the contestants, especially the loser." A smile crept into the corners of the Big Man's lips. "And I want the poem and the piece of art. Here. Delivered, and on my desk. And then I can release you from your debt of gratitude."

"Gratitude to who?" I said. "You?"

"That's right."

"For what? I thought you were just saying thank you to ME."

"Well, you DO know where you are, right?"

"Uh, the front desk at the Well of Souls?"

"That's right, Sparky. And who am I?"

"You're the Gatekeeper."

"Correct. So, I'm going to spell this out to you... You are in the Well of Souls, and I am the Gatekeeper at The Well of Souls, and I don't have to let you leave. So don't give me any shit."

I looked around at my crew. Three were staring down at their shoes. One was shaking his head and rolling his eyes.

The Gatekeeper handed me a five 10-franc notes and said, "Give this to Salim. It's the prize money for the contest. Take this hallway right over here to my left. A few twists and turns and these bozos know the way from there." The Gatekeeper looked down at his Big Book. "NEXT!" he roared, and the five of us were gone like a drafty wind as the next complainant approached the Big Desk behind us.

Salim's Place wasn't difficult to find. Robespierre said that you could fall-down drunk anywhere in Montparnasse and wake-up there. Danton added that the three exits all led to different levels and eras, and one need be very careful coming and going.

After several turns and stairs up and down, and a continual, running gripe-fest between the three velvet-clad grumblers, we approached the front entrance of Chez Salim. I had seen this place before. It had been closed. And now there were two statues at the entrance instead of only one.

...A flicker of a memory reminded me that this is where I had first seen the grumblers and the eye-roller at a reserved table in the back of the bar...

On either side of the front doors there was a stone statue of a beautiful woman holding a vase of flowers. The flowers were freshly cut and beautiful. The sign above the front doors was brightly painted. Danton and Robespierre each opened a door and the five of us entered a vibrant scene at Chez Salim.

Every square inch of the establishment was filled with patrons, laughing, dancing, drinking, talking, singing, arguing, seducing, smoking, and ordering food and drinks. The huge man behind the bar was Salim. Everybody called him by name, and he was simultaneously carrying on multiple conversations in several languages with his multicultural staff and patrons. I heard someone ask him, "Salim, how many languages DO you speak?"

"I don't know, six or seven," replied Salim. "Nine or ten when I'm drunk."

The three grumblers went right to the reserved table as if they owned it, sat down and continued arguing. Voltaire and I looked at each other knowingly. "Why do you hang around with those guys?" I asked him.

"Good question," he replied. "They are my students, and we are united at the core by our ideals. I feel responsible for them because I taught them to argue like demons. And they surpassed me. And it ended badly for them."

Salim's Place (original painting by Keith Patterson).

Voltaire looked sad. "And if they can't rest, then neither can I," he told me. "You and I are in the same boat, in this respect. I'll explain to Salim what it is that the Gatekeeper requires. Give me the prize money for the contest and I'll give it to Salim. You stay here." Voltaire held out his palm expectantly. I didn't overthink it, and in one of those moments that you might like to get back, I handed over the fistful of francs to Voltaire. As Voltaire went to the bar, I stood in the middle of a beautifully chaotic riot of sight and sound and aromas. I tried to take it all in. I thought that I recognized some faces and characters. Dali, the Surrealist painter. Kiki du Montparnasse was there, showing-off a new haircut in a low-cut dress. I saw Ernest Hemingway laughing with Henry James. Josephine Baker, the dancer, toasting the man in the hat with the big nose from a painting by Toulouse Lautrec. There were other writers and artists, a few drunks, a couple of good-natured prostitutes, musicians, and music. There was only one thing missing from this scene...my wife, Kelli.

I felt a moment of profound longing. And then she walked through the front doors of Chez Salim! She was wearing a tight red dress that I didn't recognize, and black heels that showed-off her leg muscles and made her stand-up straight in a way that really showed-off her considerable assets. She was, by far, the most beautiful woman in the room. It was my wife!

"KELLI!" I hollered across the room. I don't think she heard me.

I had no idea why she was there, at Salim's Place. I hadn't told her where I was going. Hell, I had no idea that I would be here. I waved my arm in the air to try and get her attention. All eyes were upon her. I started across the room, towards, her along with every other male in the room with a pulse. "KELLI!" I hollered as I waved my arm and squeezed my way towards her. Either she didn't hear me, or she was ignoring me.

Salim pounded his big fist upon the bar and announced "A contest! Fifty francs for first prize! Hemingway versus Picasso! Hemingway, the writer, will make art! And Picasso, the artist, will write a poem! Fifty francs to the winner by applause!" Salim produced a basket of crayons, modeling clay and paper, usually reserved for restless children. "You have one hour. The patron's applause will decide the winner. Do you, Pablo Picasso, and you, Ernest Hemingway, both agree to the terms of this contest?" The two men stepped forward. Hemingway was a hulking, bearded man with a big smile and red cheeks. Picasso, the Spanish artist, was a much smaller man, with a big head and piercing eyes. "Let's do this!" declared Hemingway.

"Agreed!" declared the fiery Spaniard.

"The contest will begin at midnight!" said Salim. You have fifteen minutes to fill your glasses and tell your lies!" The crowd roared its approval! I tried to get next to Kelli, but Picasso beat me to it. And then Hemingway, a solid wall of a man, stepped in front of me and began telling me about a story idea that he was working on. The story idea sounded vaguely familiar to me. Classic themes. Growing old. Nature. The ocean. I was listening to Ernest Hemingway's story, sort of, while trying to politely get around him and rescue my wife from Pablo Picasso's advances. I caught a glimpse of her through the crowd. Picasso was staring deeply into her eyes and speaking to her in low tones. Kelli didn't look like she needed rescuing.

Hemingway hadn't stopped talking. "I'm thinking of calling my story 'The Ancient Mariner's Boat'."

"I like your story idea," I said to Hemingway. "I think it will be quite successful. But, with all due respect, I'd like to suggest a different title."

"Yes?" Hemingway's left eyebrow was arched in annoyance.

"Instead of 'The Ancient Mariner's Boat'," I said, "how about 'The Old Man and the Sea'?"

Hemingway just glared at me.

Salim pounded his fist upon the bar, "Let the competition begin!"

Picasso and Hemingway went to the bar for materials. Hemingway chose a fistful of colored crayons and a piece of drawing paper. Picasso picked-up the writing paper, pen and ink. The two men sat down at different table and got busy creating. I looked around the bar for Kelli. She was sitting at the table with Paolo Picasso. He was staring into her eyes. She was returning the view. Picasso composed a poem as he held Kelli in his thrall.

Ernest Hemingway slashed away at his piece of drawing paper with the colorful wax crayons. The crowd of patrons, transfixed, surged towards Hemingway's table. I struggled against this tide to get to the table where Kelli sat with Picasso. The hands of the clock on the wall flew around the dial "BLAM!" Salim's giant fist slammed down upon the bar as he roared "TIME!"

Hemingway proudly held his crayon doodle aloft for the crowd to see. It was awful. The crowd scoffed and booed in drunken derision. As one, the bar patrons turned towards Picasso's table. He stood up and read his two-line poem aloud. The audience roared in laughter! It was not what Picasso was expecting. And then Picasso was gone! Vanished! He was nowhere to be seen. And neither was Kelli!

"PICASSO WINS!!" declared Salim.

"They went that way!" declared Dali, pointing towards a side door. It was another of those moments in life, where, in retrospect, I might not should have been quite so hasty as to rush off to where a Surrealist is pointing. But my blood was hot with jealousy. And out the side door of Salim's I went.

The door of Salim's side entrance slammed shut behind me. I was in the street. The street was made of mud, and blood and the screams of the terrorized and the dying. Somebody yelled, "Les Normands ont pris l'Isle de la Cite!" The Vikings have taken the City! Oh shit. No sign of Kelli or Picasso. Vikings advancing up the lane. I turned around, looking for the side entrance of Salim's. I didn't see a side door OR a Salim's. Just dry-stacked stone foundations and few standing structures. The Vikings were within spear-throwing distance. I felt something rubbing against the back of my leg. I looked down. It seemed to be my black, feral barn cat, Dodger! Then, a huge, fierce, blonde Viking brute raised his blood-stained battle axe against me! I just stood there like I was in a dream, waiting to die. And then, Dodger, like a black banshee, stepped in front of me, leaped-up and attacked the Viking's face in a whirling dervish of claws and teeth! The Viking quickly ripped Dodger from his bloody face and stomped him to death beneath his huge boot! But not before Dodger's heroic self-sacrifice gave me an extra moment, and a hand reached-out, grabbed me by the collar and pulled me inside of a dwelling! The door slammed shut behind me! I looked around. Ernest Hemingway had me by my jacket collar. I was back inside of Salim's.

"Kennard, what's your hurry? I have another story idea I'd like to share with you."

"Dodger!" I cried. "Not right now, Ernest," I replied. "My cat just got stomped to death by a Viking, I've gotta talk business with Salim, and I have to find Kelli and Picasso."

Hemingway was boring somebody else with his bullshit within nanoseconds.

Voltaire spoke up, "The contest is done and now it's time for you to help US with OUR problem."

I looked up and found Salim's gaze. He held Picasso's poem and Hemingway's doodle in his fist. 'I will keep these safe until you return for them! Do not worry, my friend. I am sure that Picasso will return with your wife! He will want to pick-up his fifty francs!" And then we were gone, out the back entrance. The old eye-roller, the three grumblers, and I were headed back to the Catacombs, to restore their bones to order, so these men could finally rest. And then I would return to Salim's Place to find my wife, retrieve the picture and the poem for the Gatekeeper and then get back to our flat and finally get some sleep.

Out the back entrance of Salim's there are cobblestones, large and irregular. Horse-drawn carriages bounce down the street, trouncing anything in their path. Men, women, and children scurry and scavenge. The fetid air smells of raw sewage. People are dressed in rags, or velvet breeches.

"Here it is!" said Voltaire and we all ducked into a low doorway and pushed past a broken door. We followed a stairway down to a long corridor which opened into an ossuary with skulls and femurs stacked neatly, from floor to ceiling, along both walls. We entered a niche off of the main hall, where Danton and Lavoisier and Robespierre each found their own bones and showed to me where the mistakes had been made by the Gatekeeper when he had interred them. The fixes were easily made. Lavoisier was taller than Robespierre and his femurs were naturally longer. Danton has an enormous block of a head. Lavoisier's bones are thin, his forehead bulbous. It was easy to locate his skull. It didn't take me long to get the three grumblers' remains in good order. They all seemed pleased. And even though Voltaire's bones weren't involved, he seemed happiest of them all.

"Thank you, Kennard," said Voltaire. And then they were gone, all four of them, like ghosts. I started back to Salim's to find Kelli and retrieve the results of the contest for the Gatekeeper.

I tried to orient myself, underground, in the Catacombs, without the help of Voltaire and the others, I ended up passing directly in front of the Gatekeeper's Big Desk. "Where is my payment?" he demanded.

"I-I haven't got it," I admitted honestly. "Salim said that he would keep Picasso's poem and Hemingway's picture in safe keeping until I returned from helping Voltaire and his friends."

The Gatekeeper shook his head disappointedly. "You can't trust anybody," he said. "So, you snuck around behind my back and rearranged their bones before paying me my price?" The Gatekeeper was not pleased.

"I need to return to Salim's Place, now," I said. "To retrieve your payment and to find my wife. The last that I saw her she was with Picasso."

"You poor, stupid bastard," said the Gatekeeper. "That was a mistake to leave your wife with Picasso. He can't be trusted. But that is YOUR problem. I still want my payment. Hemingway's artwork and a poem by Picasso."

"Your tastes are unique, Gatekeeper."

"Oh, these things are not for me."

"For who, then?" I asked.

"For my biggest client, David Grohl," replied the Gatekeeper. "He and his band are playing a concert here in the Catacombs. The Gatekeeper looked down the corridor. He pointed and said, "And here comes Dave, now!" The Gatekeeper stared at me sternly and whispered, "Dave doesn't know that you, Kennard, are contracted to retrieve these things that he desires. And it is none of his business."

Looking back subjectively, I can now see how wildly unbelievable a lot of this story might seem to be. But when David Grohl walked up to me in front of the Gatekeeper of the Well of Souls' Big Desk, stuck out his hand to shake mine and said, "Hi, my fucking name is fucking Dave Grohl." Well, that's the first moment when I really thought that I might be dreaming.

"My name is Kennard," I replied.

I knew that I could learn a lot from listening to whatever David Grohl might have to say. He is so successful, and yet seems so grounded. And thirty-nine questions about his life and craft fluttered through my brain. But, of course, I pitched him on a few of MY ideas, instead.

"I've got two movie ideas, Dave," I said

"Fuckin' lay 'em on me," he said.

"The first one is called 'Viral Destiny' and is intended to be a sequel to 'The Pick of Destiny and will also star Jacque Blanche, who is returning to Earth, riding a meteor, and rocking like Hell! The climax is when the meteor crashes into the ocean and Jacque Blanche, the rockingest virus in the universe, infects the entire planet with a VIRAL ROCK SONG, featuring you and your band and Jacque Blanche, performing my song, 'I Wanna Be, Right Where We Are'. And you can play Satan, again, if you want to, Dave. You were great in the original."

Dave smiled and nodded. The Gatekeeper looked nervous.

"What the fuck ELSE ya got?" asked Dave.

"My second movie idea could either be a stand-alone picture or a sequel to Woody Allen's 'Midnight in Paris'."

"Sounds fucking interesting," said Dave. "What's the fucking title and what the fuck is it about?"

"Well," I said. "I don't have a definite title yet. I was thinking, maybe, of 'Salim's Place'. But the movie is based on this story that we are both involved in right now."

Talk about a conversation stopper. Dave and the Gatekeeper both looked at me like I was completely out of my mind.

"Oh, Dave, one more thing. I really dug your book," I said. "It's really awesome and it helped inspire me to finish my own book, which is a collection of short stories called 90 Percent Half-True. My podcast, by the same name, promotes sales of my book. Call in to my podcast, any time. I'd love to interview you, about the things in life that you like most... about me."

Dave said, "Cool." Then he turned his attention towards the Gatekeeper, "So, did you fuckin' get me the fuckin' poem by fuckin' Picasso and the fuckin' artwork by fuckin' Hemingway?"

"Not yet," the Gatekeeper replied.

David Grohl turned on his heels and was gone.

The Gatekeeper looked down at me from behind his Big Desk. He pointed to a corridor to his left and said "Go to Salim's and retrieve my payment. NOW! Dave was more disappointed than he let on. And he's my biggest client. If you fail me, I'll haunt you to HELL and BACK and FOREVER! And, please, go rescue your wife from Pablo Picasso's clutches. He is a dog."

I needed no further encouragement from the Gatekeeper and raced to return to Chez Salim.

I had to navigate through dark places, retracing my path, and finally emerged at the front entrance of Chez Salim. One of the two statues that had been out-front was now missing. I entered. Salim was behind the bar. He was much older than I remembered him. He did not seem to recognize me.

"Salim!" I said, "it's me, Kennard."

Salim's face showed uncertainty.

"Remember the contest between Hemingway and Picasso when Hemingway made art and Picasso wrote a poem?" I asked him.

Salim scrunched his brow in thought and then his eyes lit up and he snapped his fingers as he looked me in the eyes. "Kennard," he said, "I remember you. Did you ever get your pretty wife back from Picasso's clutches?"

"Not yet," I said.

"Oh crap," said Salim. That was a long time ago."

"I need Picasso's poem and Hemingway's art, so I can give them to the Gatekeeper, so he will release me from my indebtedness to him."

"Why are you indebted to the Gatekeeper?" asked Salim.

"I'm not really sure, exactly," I said. "But I'm really exhausted. And I don't feel well. And I really just want to find my wife and get some sleep. Do you have the picture and the poem?"

"I put them somewhere safe," said Salim. He thought about it for a moment, then said, "I put them in the flower-pot of the Green Tara."

"The Green Tara?" I asked.

"The Green Tara was one of the two statues that stood out in front," explained Salim. "It is called the Green Tara because it sits in perpetual shade and has a generous coating of mosses and lichens upon her."

I opened the front door of Salim's and beheld what I already knew... the Green Tara was missing!

"Where is the Green Tara?" I asked Salim.

"She was stolen many years ago," he answered. "It was after the war. The Nazis took everything they wanted and then the Americans stole what was left."

I took off like a shot, out the front door, and retraced my crooked path back to the Big Desk of the Gatekeeper.

"Salim put the poem and the picture in the flower-pot of the Green Tara for safe-keeping, but the Green Tara was stolen, and I don't have what you want from me. And I am tired." I felt like I was about to cry. I wanted to give up.

"Here's the deal," said the Gatekeeper, "sign here." He opened his Big Book and handed me a pen. I signed my name.

"You owe me," said the Gatekeeper. "The poem by Picasso, and the picture by Hemingway. And if you give or sell them directly to David Grohl, and cut me out, I will haunt you FOREVER! DO NOT FUCK WITH ME! But I'm a reasonable man. And you don't look well. The problem seems to be right here." The Gatekeeper touched his finger to my chest, just under my breast. Searing pain tore through my body like blinding light!...

...I opened my eyes and blinked. I was breathing hard and covered in sweat. I could feel that my fever had broken. Kelli was sleeping beside me. I carefully crawled out from under the covers and went to the bathroom. I could see blood and pus dripping down my chest from a wound that I hadn't really noticed before. It looked to be the same vintage as the cat scratches on my thigh that I'd been treating. I cleaned the wound with alcohol and hydrogen peroxide and then took a hot shower. As I crawled back under the covers, I felt two-hundred-percent better.

Kelli woke up as I got back in bed. "I thought that I had lost you," I said to her as I held her in my arms.

"Awwww. You silly thing," she replied in her sweetest voice. Then we made love. In Paris. Strong, passionate love. And the angels blushed. And others sang. It's the naughty angels that sing when you make love, in Paris, as the morning light pours in through the bedroom window.

We had breakfast and packed for our return trip home. The cooked meet smell in the foyer was overpowering. I opened-up my roller bag and it was full of cooked meat! There must have been twenty pounds of boeuf bourguignon in my roller bag!

We had a plane to catch, so we didn't have time to freak-out about my roller-bag being filled with boeuf bourguignon. But it was on our minds as we trundled across the Boulevard du Montparnasse towards the Port Royal Train Station. We stopped at the same tiny bakery that we'd visited the morning of our arrival. We ordered pastries and coffees and made our breakfast. My suitcase full of meat was by my side. We were looking for a dumpster to toss it into. Suddenly a masked man appeared and snatched the meat suitcase! He left an identical one in its place! It looked just like my suitcase.

Kelli and I looked at each other. I decided to look inside the dark-blue roller bag before calling for the police. Yep. Just as I suspected. My heavy boots and long underwear. "No harm, no foul."

We paid our tab to Jean Eric, made our connections, and caught our flight back home. On the long flight back home, we watched television for a while. There was some international news. It looked like we'd gotten out of town just in time. The airport and rail stations were all shut down again. A terrorist plot to assassinate the Prime Minister as he arrived at the Senate had just been thwarted! Details were emerging that a 'MEAT SUITCASE' filled with ten kilos of boeuf bourguignon had been used to distract the guard dogs during the foiled plot! Kelli and I looked at each other with eyes wide. Then we held hands and slept most of the rest of the way back across the Atlantic.

It was great to get back home and see the animals. Connie told us that Dodger had been killed while we were away. "Was he hit by a car?" Kelli asked her.

"No," said Connie. "It looks more like he was stomped flat by a fourteen triple E."

Everybody else was fine, if a little bit sad. Everybody loved Dodger.

We buried Dodger that very day. His bloody little claws were clenched with clumps of blonde facial hair. He was lain to rest in the shade of the stone goddess on Boar's Rock. The goddess is covered in moss and lichens. A thought crossed my mind! I looked into the bowl of the water-bearer. There was something stuck in the bottom. I found a stick and fished it out what was inside. It was two folded pieces of paper, old and brittle. I unfolded them. One was a childish crayon scribble signed "E.H." The other, a poem "De l'Arc de Triomphe a la Rue Grenelle, Ta beaute est pure comme l'amour naturel." Signed "P.P." That old dog had written a love poem to my wife. Who could blame him?

I carefully refolded the two pieces of paper and gently

placed them in an old can of karma that sits upon the mantel in the Plaid Pub. Then, I met up with Kelli in the kitchen.

"I think I might have a name for the stone goddess in the donkey run," I announced.

"Oh really. What?" Kelli asked.

"The Green Tara."

Kelli shook her head affirmatively. "I'm sure there's a story behind it," she said.

"Yes, there is," I replied.

"There's a message for you on the message machine for the house phone," Kelli told me.

"Who's it from?" I asked.

"David Grohl," she said. "He left his cell number, and he wants you to call him. I wonder what HE could possibly want?"

I thought about it for about a half-second. I knew what Dave Grohl wanted.

I sure didn't want to disappoint Dave, for at least two good reasons. First, he's a nice guy and a friend of a friend. Secondly, David Grohl is possibly an Avatar of Vishnu, like Buddha, Santana, Hendrix, and Betty White. And nobody wants to disappoint an avatar of Vishnu. But my commitment was signed into the

Gatekeeper's Big Book. And he was threatening to haunt me to Hell and back. So, I knew that I needed to deliver the poem by Picasso and the picture by Hemingway to the Gatekeeper at the Well of Souls before Dave Grohl caught up to me first. "I've got an idea," I said to Kelli.

"What's up, Lover?" She replied.

"Let's go back to Paris!"

KEITH PATTERSON

THE THREE
ARROWS OF TIME

"The cosmologist strives to perceive the Mind of God and describe it as a Grand Unified Theory, or 'GUT'," began the professor. There were some rumblings and eye rolls. He was preaching to the choir. "Theoreticians of every stripe, from the cosmologists to the clerics, use these terms interchangeably. But, as this lecture will demonstrate, these terms are not synonymous, and the GUT will be considered the more expansive construct."

The audience in the University's Lecture Hall grumbled and harrumphed at the professor's flirtation with blasphemy. "What could be greater than The Mind of God?"

"Sanctimonious Fool!"

"Charlatan!"

"Democrat!" Several in attendance stood-up and began to leave the Hall.

The professor cleared his throat, raised his voice, and continued, "Einstein said 'there are two certainties in this existence, an expanding Universe, and the stupidity of Man. And I'm not so sure about the Universe.' I will make a definitive assertion as to Einstein's first point before you confirm his assumptions regarding the second." The professor looked out from the lectern and made eye-contact with some of his esteemed colleagues. He had their attentions and delivered his haymaker. "I believe that Einstein was right to not be sure that the Universe is expanding. It only APPEARS to be expanding."

"Are you daft?"

"This is pure insanity!"

"What lunacy is this?"

Nobody was leaving the Lecture Hall. The professor had them just where he wanted them, and he continued. "Imagine a linear illustration of our expanding and contracting Physical Universe as a Wave that forms, crests, crashes and then repeats the cycle. We are tiny particles floating along inside of the Wave as it is approaching the shore. From our perspective, as our Wave crests, it appears to be stretching out and expanding in all-directions away from us, when, in actuality, the Wave has already crested and is collapsing in upon itself. The crashing of the Wave represents our Physical Universe collapsing into The Singularity which defines the Finite Boundaries of this current Physical Universe. What happens at The Singularity? Hawking asserts that all information is lost and on this point he and I must disagree. Nothing is lost, only changed. And when the Three Arrows of Time, as first described by Hawking and with improvements that I will define, intersect at the coming Singularity, Time equals Consciousness. Energy, freed from equaling MC squared because of the total collapse of the Physical Universe, is available to illuminate Consciousness. Energy X Consciousness = the Mind of God."

The Lecture Hall was abuzz with indignant asides and discussion. "Coming Singularity?"

"What nonsense!"

"There, you said it yourself. It's the Mind of God that we're looking for. What could be greater than that?"

"Yeah!"

"Yeah! How could the GUT be greater than the MOG?"

"Imagine, if you will," began the professor, "the synaptic moment in-between Physical Universes, when Total Consciousness is illuminated, and we behold the Mind of God. Einstein will be partially vindicated as Relativity guarantees that the Mind of God will be seeking to behold the Mind of Its God and so-on and so-forth ad-infinitum. In our moment of Total Enlightenment, we will see that for every new thing that we know there is even more that we cannot know. The ratio of what we know to what we don't know is like Heisenberg's Uncertainty Principle inverted X Expansion. But it's not what Einstein got right that is the central theme of this lecture. And I will now explain how a deeper examination of the boundary conditions of Hawking's Three Arrows of Time proves that this current Physical Universe is now in full collapse."

"You're taking-on Einstein AND Hawking?"

"Pompous fake!"

"Lunatic."

"Heretic."

The professor continued undeterred, "Hawking describes the Three Arrows of Time as the Boundary Conditions for our existence and this concept is very useful as a part of the framework of the GUT, but he doesn't order the Three Arrows cohesively or develop them sufficiently. So, in order of appearance in a New Universe, here is a revised description of the Three Arrows of Time."

"The First Arrow of Time is the arrow of Expansion and Collapse. As a New Universe bursts forth from The Singularity, the First Arrow of Time departs from Consciousness in the Non-Physical Universe and enters the New Universe as Expansion. The New Universe knows how to expand because Consciousness, the repository of All Knowledge relative to our perspective in the Sum of All Realities, enters the New Universe as the First Arrow of Time."

"When the Boundary Conditions imposed by Consciousness on the First Arrow of Time have shifted its arc of Expansion into the parameters of its imminent Collapse then the Expansion of the New Universe will have slowed down enough for Matter to form and accrete, and the Second Arrow of Time departs from Consciousness in the Non-Physical Universe and enters the New Universe as Accretion. At this point, when Matter begins to Accrete, the New Universe has become a Physical Universe."

"While the Physical Universe is in its Accretion stage, planets and galaxies and solar systems are forming and coalescing and conditions are too intense and extreme to allow Living Things to exist. When the Second Arrow of Time has shifted from Accretion to Entropy then conditions are ripe in the Physical Universe for the Third Arrow of Time to enter the Physical Universe as the first Living Thing. As a Boundary Condition of our own existence, we know that the Third Arrow of Time has entered into this Physical Universe because we are Living Things. We can induce that the Second Arrow of Time has shifted from Accretion to Entropy because of the same line of reasoning, and thus, it logically follows that because we know that the Second Arrow of Time is now Entropic we can be assured that the First Arrow of Time has shifted from Expansion and is well into to its Collapse. The metaphorical Wave has crested and the Three Arrows of Time are rushing at the rate of inverted Expansion towards intersection at the Coming Singularity where they will, once again, become Total Consciousness, which will be Illuminated by all of the Energy in this Universe to reveal the Mind of God, before the cycle begins anew, once again, with the First Arrow of Time leaving Consciousness in the Non-Physical Universe to enter a New Universe with a Big Bang of Expansion. And so, visualizing the Three Arrows of Time as the framework of an Expanding and Contracting, Accreting and Entropic and now Living Universe, the Cosmological nature of the GUT is fairly straight-forward. My Grand Unified Theory is the framework for the Revelations of many Minds of God, from the sub-Quantum to the ad Infinite. And now I shall take some questions before we take a short intermission."

The Three Arrows of Time
(original painting by Keith Patterson).

The Q and A session became a bit unruly as the disbelieving mob dragged the professor through the burning coals of their jealousies and small-mindedness. After the dissatisfied crowd finally allowed the emotionally and physically exhausted theorist to take an intermission, he collapsed on a bench outside the venue beside a little old lady who was feeding the pigeons while intermittently blowing her nose into a stained handkerchief.

After a lengthy silence, the theorist spoke to the little, old lady, "I'm giving a lecture, inside, and it's not going so well."

The little old lady threw some seeds on the sidewalk in front of the bench, blew her nose into her handkerchief and replied, "I know. I was in there."

The theorist turned towards the little old lady and said, "Really? Well, what did you think of my lecture, so far?"

After a considerable pause the little old lady threw out some more seed, again blew her nose into her handkerchief and replied, "Your Grand Unified Theory is a load of crap! And the Universe is NOT just a load of crap!" The woman threw out some more seed and blew her nose into her hankie.

"Oh really?" replied the theorist. "Well, what is it then?"

"It's turtles," replied the little old lady. "Turtles from

the ground up."

The theorist cocked his head thoughtfully to one side and considered the potentially profound quantum and cosmological implications of what the woman was saying as she threw out some more bird seed and once again blew her nose into her hankie. He turned to her and said, "That's really quite interesting. May I use that?"

The old woman looked at her filthy hankie, abruptly got up from the bench and began ambling away. She looked back over her shoulder and replied, "Get your own snot rag, you weirdo!"

The professor made his way back inside the Lecture Hall, regained the podium and continued his lecture. "Consider the symbol for Infinity, it is the Mobius Loop. It is the shape of the metaphorical turtle, the shape of the Quantum String, the shape of the electron's potentiality, the shape of the Magnetic Field and the shape of the finite boundaries of the limitless Universe. The synaptic core of every Mobius construct, from the Quantum to the Cosmological, is where matter changes to anti-matter, negative to positive, light to dark, left to right and so on and so forth, up and down the scales of Relativity. The Cosmological Universe is an enormous magnetic field that reverses polarity every 15-Billion or so of our Earth years. The point at which the poles of the Physical Universe reverse is analogous to the Singularity. And on the quantum level, the atom and the string are constructed the same way as the Cosmological Universe. So, if we know the size of an atom, the duration of its stability and the duration of its electron's synaptic apotheosis, and we also know the scale of the Quantum Planck length relative to the atom, then we can extrapolate Cosmologically using the inverse of the same scale and estimate the duration of the synapse of THE Singularity as well as projecting the duration of this Physical Universe and our Current Relative Time Space Location."

"Could you repeat that?"

"Yes, please. The current, relative... wha?"

"Our Current Relative Time Space Location. Please try and keep-up. I've got a train to catch." The professor took a breath and got to the meat of his lecture. He had the attentions of what was left of his audience.

"And now, we arrive at Deep-space Background Radiation Interference Patterns."

"Why is the Physical Universe exactly where it is and not one foot to the left or right? Because, in its Expansion stage, the First Arrow of Time follows the path of least resistance. Previous cycles of Expansion and Collapse have left residue in the imperfect vacuum of Space that interferes with subsequent cycles of Expansion and Collapse. Each New Physical Universe is in a different, partially over-lapping place than the previous one. The skewed, intersecting, over-lapping lines of multiple magnetic fields of past Physical Universes that fill our Current Physical Universe are responsible for the Deep-Space Background Radiation Interference Patterns that are testimony to what has come before."

"And that leads us to the Nuclear, Gravitational and Electro-magnetic Forces."

"At the Big Bang Creation of a New Universe, after The Singularity that followed the collapse of the Previous Physical Universe explodes forth, there is just the First Arrow of Time in the New Universe and only the Nuclear Force exists in the New Universe. As the First Arrow of Time shifts from Expansion to Collapse and the Second Arrow of Time enters the Physical Universe and Matter begins to accrete, the Nuclear Force still exists but the Gravitational Force is ascendant. As the Second Arrow of Time shifts from Accretion to Entropy and the Third Arrow of Time enters the Physical Universe as the First Living Thing, the Gravitational Force and the Nuclear Force still exist but the Electro-Magnetic Force becomes ascendant. As the Collapse of the Physical Universe gains momentum, the Gravitational Force is, once again, ascendant. And then, as the Physical Universe nears THE Singularity and crosses over the Cosmological Event Horizon, the Nuclear Force is again exclusive. Analysis of deep-space background radiation interference patterns to determine the ratios of ascendancy from these interactions of Forces can be used to postulate as to our

Relative position in the arc of the Collapse of this Current Physical Universe."

The professor paused for a moment, took a drink of water from a glass of water, and then blew his nose into his handkerchief.

The audience were murmuring. Someone down in front asked, "So you're absolutely certain that the Physical Universe is in full collapse?"

"Absolutely," answered the professor.

"That's all a bit depressing."

"Not really," said the professor, "the collapsing Universe is actually the Good News."

""What?""

"How could that be?" The audience was restive.

"The coming Singularity," replied the theorist, "is the scientist's opportunity to perceive the Mind of God in relation to the GUT. And make special note that I said 'perceive'."

That got the audience in a lather. They were one misspoken quip from erupting into an angry mob.

"Now that I have your attention," continued the professor. "Allow me to mesh the sacred with the secular and quote from the New Testament as I attempt to explain."

"The New Testament?"

"The bloody-well Bible?"

"What is this?"

"We thought this was a scientific lecture!"

"Rubbish!"

"Yeah, RUBBISH!"

"ACTUALLY," began the professor, taking back command of the lecture hall, "we will begin with the very last book of the Bible, Revelation, where is mentioned the 'Second Death'."

"Second Death?"

"As if one's not enough?"

"You are correct, indeed. One death is not enough. For the physical death of our earthly bodies is but the first death. Disembodied souls exist in a transitional realm. Those who cling to the remembered sensations of corporeal life dwell in a purgatorial existence. Only by abandoning slavery to sensation can one move on to the realm of perception. Sensation negates perception."

'"Sensation negates perception?"

"Well, that's just plain ignorance!"

"Wait," said the professor. "Allow me to explain. We

can all recite the five temporal senses and understand what they are. But we speak of a "sixth sense", a knowingness that defies simple categorization amongst the first five. To experience this sixth sense is to get a glimpse at "perception". Total Perception requires freedom from the prejudices and assumptions that naturally arise from reliance upon sensation."

The professor paused.

"What about the second death?" someone shouted.

"I was just getting to that," replied the professor. "Artificial Intelligence is becoming integrated into every aspect of our existence and the lines between men and machines are already blurred. And, likewise, as we attempt to upload consciousness to machines and create our own ethereal eternity, the line between A.I. eternity and the purgatorial first-death stage of existence will be blurred. The Singularity, or Second Death, will erase AI Consciousness and allow Original Consciousness to coalesce and reform."

The lecturing professor cleared his throat and blew his nose into his hankie. He was catching a cold and was late for his train. "That concludes my lecture. I'm sorry, but I have no time to answer questions." The professor gathered his things as the audience grumbled and murmured.

"Can we attain Original Consciousness without being consumed by the Singularity?" someone shouted out as the professor turned to leave the stage.

The professor sneezed, again, into his handkerchief and replied, "In essence, the Singularity IS Original Consciousness."

"The Singularity is Original Consciousness? Wow. Do you mind if I use that?" asked the inquisitive audience member.

The professor looked down at his dirty hankie, smiled and replied. "Get your own snot-rag, you weirdo."

THE CLOCK TOWER

A vivid dream…

Everything I own is either in my car or strapped down on top. I'm at a gas station filling-up my fuel-tank while every good-time buddy or pretty face I've ever known is trying to drag me to a party or into a hotel saloon. I can see the Clock Tower off in the distance, its hands moving resolutely towards the top of the hour when the enormous gate of the great city will be closed forever. A newly elected regime is taking over and when the gate slams shut no one will be allowed to leave or enter the city ever again.

My car's big fuel-tank takes time to fill. The gate to the city is moving in a huge, slow arc. My drinking buddies and paramours are relentless in their pursuits of my attentions. I figure I might have time for ONE beer while my gas-tank gets completely filled-up.

One beer turns into a celebration. There are no clocks on the walls inside the Hotel Saloon. When a new customer opens the front door, I notice that the light from inside floods the darkness outside. The sun has gone down. I break free from the easy clutches of fast friends and run outside to collect my car, but it's no longer parked at the gas station. Someone has stolen my car and I can see him, up ahead, shifting gears and heading for the city gate.

I have the angle and run as fast as I can to catch-up with the thief who is stealing my car. I hop over fences, dodge traffic and little old ladies and catch-up with my vehicle, clutching at and grabbing the front passenger's door panel. The car-thief levels a revolver at my forehead and I release my hold on the passenger's door! The thief drives away in my car, accelerating and heading for the closing city gate.

The city gate is nearly closed. I can see that the thief and my stolen car will barely make it out. I realize that I cannot make it to the gate on-foot before it closes. But I CAN make it to the Clock Tower, where a Royal Progression is entering a door at its base. The leader of this Royalty is wearing a long, flowing robe and is surrounded by armed guards. This royal arbiter will preside over the change of power and usher-in a malevolent reign. I run as hard as I can to catch-up to the Royal Progression as the last guard enters the closing door. I dive for the door and catch hold of a piece of fabric. It is the corner of the flowing robe worn by the Royal Arbiter.

The door to the Clock Tower cannot shut because of my grip on the corner of the Royal Arbiter's robe. Then the door is flung open. I land on my back and a dozen fierce guards have their razor-sharp spearheads at my throat. The Royal Arbiter looks down at me with a scornful countenance. I know that my life hangs in the balance, and I am in violation of all protocol.

"WHAT DO YOU HAVE TO SAY FOR YOURSELF?" barks the Royal Arbiter!

I think hard… "I'm a… a musician?"

There is a terrible and endless moment in-between heartbeats. The Arbiter remains fierce. His guards' spear-tips remain at my throat. An angel appears. I know her but I can't place her face.

"He's alright," says the angel to the Arbiter.

The guards relax. The Royal Arbiter smiles and begins writing on a piece of paper. "A musician, huh? Well, here's a lyric for you." He hands me the piece of paper, turns and hurries to his royal task as I begin rolling like a tumbleweed, out through the city gate, just before it slams shut, and the Clock Tower strikes the top of the hour.

I am outside of the city, temporarily safe from the malevolent administration gathering strength like a killer storm within. I have nothing left in this world but the clothes on by back… and a piece of paper clutched in my hand.

The piece of paper given me by the Royal Arbiter seems to be blank. I look more closely and see many tiny written lines on both sides of the piece of paper.

When I stare at one line, it grows large enough to read and then recedes when I concentrate on the next line. Each line is written in a different language and in many different alphabets and scripts. It is every written language this world has ever known. And every line reads the same. "God is Love."

ACKNOWLEDGEMENTS

Thank you to the God of all of us who works through the many that have helped me, thus far, on my pathway through this lifetime.

Thank you to my wife and partner, Kelli Scarrow Patterson, for your steadfast love and encouragement, and for your hard work in helping me to realize my creative vision, finish this manuscript and publish this book. From inception to completion, this task would have never happened without you. I love you to infinity and then some.

Many thanks to the Cosmic Mojemians, Scott and Anna Nurmi, for all of the fun and hard work at Mojo Factory Productions. To Jennifer Welliver and David Lillard at the Clarke Monthly for encouraging, editing, and publishing me. To Morgan Morrison, Sarah Ames and Nathan Borger at Barns of Rose Hill for aiding and abetting my creative schemes. To Julie Ashby, Steve Scott, and Cristopher VanMeter at Hip and Humble Interiors for selling so many of my paintings, for finding us the Green Tara, and for making me cry my own tears of mirthful indiscretion. To Bridget and Sean Peck, for keeping me alive, and Rodney Barnes, for inspiration. Ted and Caroline Aschenbrenner, for being there... Big Lare, for being a great mentor, and Dan Dan the Roller Man. The T.J.T., The West Coast gang, J.J., Ashley, Steven, Jimbo and Bonnie, Jayne, Rhonda, Carrie, Kathy, Gabby and Melissa. To H. Baker, for friendship, encouragement and insightful edits, Jean Wilson Jean Wilson, for sharing a trick to help me remember names, the rest of the book club, Laurine, Jessie, Chris, and Brenda. To Annie M. Patterson, for giving me two fine kids, AliSue and N8 the 4th, who make us both very proud. To Roderick Krause, for a whole lot of working side by side. Mark Lemmon, for being my favorite pirate, Mike Kidd, for actually being the VP of Karma in the Can Inc. To Scott and Denise Kidd, and to Pat Craig and Michelle Robinson for always supporting my creative efforts. To the Drewmer, for rockin' hard, and to Carole, for keepin' him rockin'. To Ken Logwood, Ken Schubert, John "Willy" Williams, Eileen McIntyre, Dave "Watty" and Caroline Watkins, Diane and Bob Mathias, Mark Metcalf, Greenie and Cindy, Pat Curtin and all of their family and friends that have touched me. You guys are my moral center. And yes, that is an oxymoron. To my brother, Chris, his wife Donna, my sister Amy and her husband Steve, and all of their families, and all of my wonderful Aunts, Uncles, Nieces, Nephews and Cousins, too many to name here. I am a product of your love and laughter. Special thanks to my late Uncle Phil. To my nephews, Alex Patterson and James Lavinder, and my double cousin, Phillip Herndon, for all the great conversations before I got moved to the grown-ups' table.

A special thanks to my parents, Nathan and Mary Sue. It was a great run while we had it.

ABOUT THE AUTHOR

Nathan "Keith" Patterson III was born March 1st, 1959, in Danville, Virginia, to Mary Sue and Nathan Jr. Keith went to Grade School in Northern Virginia and Southern Mississippi, Middle School and High School were completed in Alexandria, Virginia. And a BA in Psychology was earned from George Mason University in 1985. Keith now lives with his wife and partner, Kelli, at Kastle Keep Farm in Berryville, Virginia, with their crew of horses, donkeys, cats, and dogs. Keith Patterson is also a professional artist with a growing list of clients and collectors nationally and the Cosmic Harvest Gallery, which features his work, resides in a stand-alone building on the farm.

Made in the USA
Middletown, DE
03 March 2022